W9-CQD-612

OVERSIZE TS 820 .B37 1983
Becksvoort, Christian.
In harmony with wood
36313   2195

WILLIAM T. BOYCE LIBRARY
FULLERTON COLLEGE
FULLERTON, CALIF. 92634

JEMCO

IN
HARMONY
WITH WOOD

CHRISTIAN BECKSVOORT

IN
HARMONY
WITH WOOD

VNR **VAN NOSTRAND REINHOLD COMPANY**
New York Cincinnati Toronto London Melbourne

This book is written in memory of
Max Cook of Luray, Virginia.

Copyright © 1983 by Christian Becksvoort
Library of Congress Catalog Card Number 82-13683
ISBN 0-442-21339-5

All rights reserved. No part of this work covered by the copyright hereon may be reproduced or used in any form or by any means—graphic, electronic, or mechanical, including photocopying, recording, taping, or information storage and retrieval systems—without written permission of the publisher.

Printed in the United States of America
Designed by Laura Bernay
Photos and illustrations by the author, unless otherwise noted.

Published by Van Nostrand Reinhold Company Inc.
135 West 50th Street
New York, New York 10020

Van Nostrand Reinhold
480 Latrobe Street
Melbourne, Victoria 3000, Australia

Van Nostrand Reinhold Company Limited
Molly Millars Lane
Wokingham, Berkshire RG11 2PY, England

16 15 14 13 12 11 10 9 8 7 6 5 4 3 2 1

Library of Congress Cataloging in Publication Data

Becksvoort, Christian.
  In harmony with wood.

  Bibliography: p. 130
  Includes index.
  1. Wood. 2. Woodwork. I. Title.
TS820.B37   1983   634.9   82-13683
ISBN 0-442-21339-5

CONTENTS

OVERSIZE
TS
820
B37
1983.

FOREWORD   vii

PREFACE   ix

CHAPTER 1. TREES AND WOOD TECHNOLOGY   1

CHAPTER 2. WOOD AND TREE IDENTIFICATION
            AND CHARACTERISTICS   15

CHAPTER 3. WOODLOT MANAGEMENT AND HARVEST   76

CHAPTER 4. SAWING AND DRYING WOOD   90

CHAPTER 5. WORKING WITH SOLID WOOD   104

BIBLIOGRAPHY   130

INDEX   132

36313

WILLIAM T. BOYCE LIBRARY
FULLERTON COLLEGE
Fullerton, California 92634

FOREWORD

Even though it has been ten years since we moved into the home we designed and built "with our own two hands," many of the same thoughts continue to repeat themselves each time I look around it. One of the most frequent of those thoughts is the recollection that, until my thirtieth year, I knew absolutely nothing about wood. I scarcely knew where it came from, much less how to analyze its strengths and recognize its weaknesses. That is what can happen to a fellow who is raised in the city and educated in classrooms.

In that thirtieth year, however, I began my apprenticeship as a commercial fisherman, and wood was what kept us afloat. With scarcely any capital at our disposal, my partners and I had to make do with whatever boats we could acquire at incidental prices or, quite often, merely in return for hauling the wrecks out of a boatyard.

For seven years I restored, repaired, and rebuilt ancient and abused wooden watercraft, and in the course of that education I became acquainted with most of the different kinds of wood, with their vagaries and frustrations as well as strengths and needs. I painted wood, scraped it, sanded it, drilled it, steamed it, caulked it, nailed it, fastened it, and fashioned it into stems, sterns, planks, masts, booms, hatch covers, tables, door frames, tackle boxes, net carriers, engine beds, and clam rake handles. Everything from mahogany, oak, pine, cedar, spruce, teak, cypress, and ash suffered under my clumsy hands.

By the time I departed that career, older, wiser, but still a zealous fisherman, I had learned a bit about wood. I had learned that oak is stringy, heavy, and strong; that one sands with the grain; that large nails driven near the ends of planks will usually split those planks; that spruce is lighter than ash (and therefore better for oars); that even a bit of rot in a mast will weaken it; that wood and water react in wondrous ways; that even relatively delicate lengths of wood, if properly fashioned, can be incredibly strong and resilient enough to resist the battering of awesome seas.

I also discovered and learned to appreciate the enduring beauty of wood as is, unpainted and unstained.

Wood is one of the great, largely unrecognized natural resources of this nation. There are many places on this globe where wood is a rarity, where the burning of oak logs in a picnic bonfire would be considered as wanton as skipping gold coins into a deep lake. But in America, we take wood for granted. Many of us can live thirty years or more without even understanding its origins and its character.

I am no longer quite that ignorant, and I thank my fishermen friends for the insights they helped me gain. From those beginnings, I developed a love for wood that still grows. I find sensuality in the texture of a well-sanded, well-oiled plank. I am captivated by the aesthetics of knots, grain, and hue. I am inspired by wood's organic immortality; it never dies. With every change in temperature, with every ray of sunshine, drop of rain, breath of salt fog, or splash of ocean spray, wood responds. It swells, shrinks, curls, changes color; it reacts as if the soul of the tree still locked within it has never departed, but is there, reaching and responding to the presence of moisture just as the parent tree did every day of its life in the forest.

Wood is a renewable and immortal resource. It is never still. Unlike steel, aluminum, plastic, stone, or brick, wood moves. It is alive, it glows, and, if you care for it, wood will shelter you with maintenance-free strength, wood will warm you, wood will please your eye, and wood will wrap you in its immortal strength when you go to your grave. Nature has provided us with no better structural material. Wood needs only to remain dry or be well ventilated if it becomes wet. It is best to keep it dry and ventilated, and to rub it with natural oils now and then to replace those it has lost in the process of separation from the tree.

Wooden doors, frames, and furniture buried with the ancients of Egypt several thousand years ago are still as strong, functional, and lovely as the day the tombs were closed. So you need not worry about "old" wood. If you understand grain, can judge which kind of wood might be best for what sort of purpose; if you know the varieties and can sense something of the wonder of wood's immortality, wood will do well by you and your home.

Let me tell you one wood story.

The new owners of our former home wanted our dining room table when we sold that place, so we left it for them. During the six months we worked before we could move to our new home, I forgot the missing piece of furniture. Our first supper in the new place was eaten from a small picnic table borrowed from a friend. It was not large enough for all the family together.

The next day I rummaged in the lumber pile in front of the still-abuilding house. We constructed the house primarily with planks and timbers taken from two large Maine barns which, in turn, had been built more than a century before. Their present owner wanted them down; he was going to bulldoze and burn them. That seemed such a waste to us. We wanted our home to minimize waste rather than stress consumption. The wood worked well.

But some of it has been difficult to find a function for. There were heavy hemlock planks, for example, that had come from the floors of the cow stalls. More than an inch thick and better than twenty-two inches wide, the planks had been battered by hooves and soaked with urine and cow manure.

To me, in my impatience to get a family table built, the hemlock seemed made to order. I took three planks. Their massive, collective breadth totaled more than five feet. With a nail driven in the center, a string, and a bit of chalk, I drew a circle across the breadth, cut along the line with a saber saw, sanded the planks down ¼ inch, and mounted the three-piece disk atop a square frame built of barn timbers.

The table was meant to be temporary, but it was strong enough so I could dance around its edge, handsome enough so no one wanted to let it go. Rubbed with linseed oil every several weeks, and brushed by scores of hands every day for ten years of meals, the hemlock has acquired a lovely soft patina. It glows under candles in the evening, shines in the morning sunrise.

Those hemlock planks served the creatures of the manger for more than a century; now they serve us just as well, and will continue to serve longer than we will live. Wood is always beautiful, always immortal. You only have to know that to know how to treat it. You will never know all the uses it can be put to.

You can, however, make a start by learning a bit more about it by reading this book.

JOHN N. COLE

From *From the Ground Up* by John N. Cole and Charles Wing, illustrations by Tom Paiment. Copyright © 1976 by John N. Cole and Charles Wing. Reprinted by permission of Little, Brown in association with the Atlantic Monthly Press.

PREFACE

This book covers a tremendous amount of territory. Perhaps it is too ambitious a project; perhaps not ambitious enough. It is intended to give the woodworker an understanding of some of the many aspects of wood properties, growth, harvest, and production. The key to working harmoniously with wood is understanding. The various steps in wood growth, processing, and utilization should be understood by all involved. The woodlot manager must be familiar with the woodworker's needs. The sawyer should know what the wood is intended for, and how best to saw it to suit that purpose. The kiln operator must know the type of wood, how it was sawn, and the end product.

The woodworker can then fashion the wood into boats, rakes, harpsichords, sleds, sculptures, barns, flutes, doors, baskets, chairs, cabinets, candleholders, gunstocks, dulcimers, wagons, tables, looms, cradles, bowls, or ax handles.

Appreciation, too, comes from following through the *entire* process: from planting a tree, pruning it, watching it grow, cutting it, drying it, shaping and jointing the wood, to finally finishing it. Understanding comes from years of experience and familiarity with a few species.

The worth of a finished object is not necessarily in the wood used, but how well and intelligently it is used. Wood is too precious a resource to be wasted through incompetence.

This book is intended for the woodworker and cabinetmaker. The first four chapters deal with subjects not often covered in woodworking texts. These chapters serve as introductions to wood structure, tree identification, woodlot management, harvest, sawing, and drying of wood. The final chapter more closely examines solid wood construction. A rudimentary understanding of cabinetry and joinery is assumed. While multitudes of books deal with these subjects already, few tackle the concept of wood *movement* as it applies directly to cabinet work. Shrinkage and expansion are inevitable, and must be taken into account when planning, gluing, making joints, and assembling the finished piece. Since there are usually several ways of achieving the same end, the actual construction process, the method, is subjective, and drawn not only from my own experience, but from that of others, as well as the tried and true methods of traditional joinery.

I would like to give my sincerest thanks to the following persons: Barbara Ravage of Van Nostrand Reinhold, who carefully edited each chapter, and who offered her help, suggestions, and criticism throughout; Thomas Moser, not only for his proofreading, encouragement, and inspiration, but also for the use of his furniture and workshop for many of the photos in this book; Abe Dulberg, for his quality work in the printing of all my photographs, his helpful suggestions, and the use of his equipment; John Limbach of Ripon Microslides, for his thirty excellent photomicrographs; John Cole, for allowing me to use portions of *From the Ground Up* as a foreword; Al Kirk of the University of Southern Maine, for his teaching, proofreading, technical help, and use of his reference material; and the staff at the U.S. Forest Products Laboratory, Madison, WI, for their generous technical help and assistance.

Special thanks should also go to the many others who made this effort possible: Mark Gustafson of Washington, DC; Antonios Perros of Silver Spring, MD; Tom Barrett of Unicorn Universal Woods, Ltd., Toronto, Canada; Jim Marvy of Hopkins, MN; Alexander Disdier of Ridgecrest, CA; Charles Annibel of Shenandoah National Park, VA; Warren Ross of Hampstead, NH; Dr. Ralph Griffin of the University of Maine, Orono, ME; Michael deLesseps of Freeport, ME; Duncan Howlett of Center Lovell, ME; Karen Gustafson of the Maine Nature Conservancy, Brunswick, ME; Theresa Shostak of Lewiston, ME; John Ackerman of Durham, ME; Jim Ledger of New Gloucester, ME; Malcolm Berry of New Gloucester, ME; Nancy Fisher of New Gloucester, ME; Willow Schwarz of New Gloucester, ME; Owen Haskell of New Gloucester, ME.

A final word of thanks to my wife, Margaret, who not only offered unlimited help and encouragement and located much of the reference material, but who also managed to have our first child during that time.

My sincerest gratitude to all.

CHAPTER 1

TREES AND WOOD TECHNOLOGY

Trees have always held a certain fascination. These, the largest living organisms on the planet, are symbols of strength, hope, and renewal. They combine graceful beauty and utility, providing mankind with sustenance and a warmth that is both physical and psychological. More than the basic necessities of life, trees provide us with a link to the natural world. In no way is this natural mystique better personified than in the wood itself, in the infinite combinations of color and grain. This variety, so pleasing to the eye, is all the more appreciated in today's world of plastic. Yet the average modern man has less knowledge of the nature and characteristics of solid wood than his less educated ancestors did.

WOOD ANATOMY

The woodworker, especially, must be aware of the anatomy of the tree: the leaves, roots, and branches. Each of these plays an important role in the tree's growth and ultimately in the raw material, wood. A familiarity with the cellular structure of the tree leads to a better understanding of what actually constitutes wood and why it behaves as it does. Knowledge of the properties of wood is most important. What causes color, taste, and odor, and how does it affect the wood's intended use? What is the difference between density and specific gravity, and how does this relate to weight and hardness of wood? What are the causes of some of the more common defects in wood, and how can one avoid them or work with them? An in-depth understanding leads to a better, more rational use of this versatile material.

ROOTS

A tree's root system serves four basic functions: absorption, conduction, storage, and anchorage. Roots absorb water and inorganic salts. Water is vital to plants for respiration and photosynthesis, and is also an essential element in protoplasm. It is used in transportation of raw material, including oxygen and carbon dioxide. Water is taken in directly through the root hairs, the smallest yet most active portion of the root system. Because inorganic salts can be absorbed only when in solution, water is necessary for this purpose too. Once inside the roots, the solution can be transported to the rest of the tree, as needed.

Roots also act as storage areas. Excess sugar manufactured in the leaves is stored in the roots (and sapwood) over the winter, until needed for leaf development the following spring.

Roots are well adapted to holding the tree in place. The root hairs, rootlets, and branch roots form a network that firmly grips rocks and soil particles. A few roots are programmed by hormones to grow more or less in a downward direction (positive geotropism) whereas most roots grow away from the vertical (plagiotropism). Small roots will grow into rock crevices and exert tremendous pressure, eventually splitting the rock apart.

Root systems differ in configuration. The two principal types are fibrous and tap root systems. A fibrous root mass is composed of many branching roots usually growing no deeper than a few feet below ground and extending beyond the edge of the branches. Trees with fibrous roots include most maples, firs, beech, locust, and redwood. Tall trees like firs, with fibrous roots growing in shallow soil, are usually the first to blow down during heavy winds.

Trees with tap roots have one major root that grows straight down to depths of 15 to 20 feet (4.5−6.1 m). Masses of fibrous feeder roots grow out of the tap root, but the entire system is not nearly as shallow as a fibrous system. Hickories, pines, oaks, sweetgum, and walnut have tap roots, making them difficult to transplant after the seedling reaches a certain age. In areas of rocky, ledgy soil, these trees do not develop tap roots, but form almost a fibrous system.

A tree's roots comprise about 10 percent of its total mass. The combined length of the roots often reaches hundreds of miles, a much larger network than the branches. In a few cases, roots can act as regenerative organs. Black locust, for instance, will sprout from suckers (shoots from root buds) around the trunk.

From a woodworker's utilitarian point of view, the value of roots is limited; very little research has been done on root properties and potential uses. Occasionally, the clump of roots just below the trunk can be salvaged, and sometimes will be used for veneer. Root burls of the Erica species are fashioned into pipe briars, and some root cross-sections can be used for inlay work.

BRANCHES

Although twigs and branches account for only 10−15 percent of a tree's total volume; they are usually the first noticed and appear to be the most important. From the tree's point of view, however, they are merely a superstructure for holding leaves. Branches expose leaves as evenly as possible to all available sunlight. Each species has a distinct pattern and spacing.

Twigs are extremely useful in tree identification. They may be very slender as in cherry and maple, or thick and stubby as in walnut and ash. The bud shapes are also different from each species, the location of the bud determining the location of the new twigs. Therefore, buds opposite each other will grow into opposite twigs, as in ash and maple, whereas alternate buds will form alternate twigs, as in locust. Occasionally, buds will be whorled, three to a group, equally spaced around a twig, as in catalpa.

Vertical growth that gives branches their length and trees their height originates from the leader buds at the ends of twigs. The actual area of growth inside the leader bud is called the apical meristem.

Twigs and branches form knots in the wood. Starting as a bud on the young trunk, the new twig grows laterally. As the tree grows, new wood is formed around the trunk and the branch, one layer or ring each year. Thus, the branch becomes an integral part of the wood. When that portion of the trunk is cut into boards, the branch appears as a tight or red knot. On the other hand, if the branch is killed, either by insects, disease, shade, or intentional pruning, the trunk will continue to grow around the branch while the dead stub remains the same size. Eventually, the wood grows completely around and over the dead branch (see "Pruning," p. 83). A dead knot in a board is loose and black in color. Branch stubs will often start to decay before they are completely covered by new wood growth. When these decayed black knots appear in boards, they will often fall out, leaving a knot hole. Since black and red knots are frequently present in the same board, and since knots are usually denser than the surrounding wood and have a grain that runs contrary to the grain of the board, they are considered defects by all lumber grading systems.

On the whole, branches, like roots, are of no great value to the woodworker. Since branches seldom grow perfectly upright, they consist mainly of reaction wood, which shrinks and warps excessively (see "Reaction Wood," p. 12). This makes the wood less than ideal for most work, although branch wood may be suitable for carvings, bases, plaques, and other small objects. Unless branches are the only source of wood available, the effort of cutting, sawing, and drying is rarely worth the resulting product for most woodworking purposes. For firewood, however, branches contain the same number of BTUs per pound of wood as does the trunk, and often do not even need to be split.

LEAVES

Leaves and needles are the food manufacturing organs of the tree. Leaf cells contain green chloroplasts, which in turn contain chlorophyll. Plants are the only living organisms that can convert sunlight into sugar. Carbon dioxide is absorbed through openings in the undersides of the leaves. Water from the roots is brought to the leaves and is catalyzed with the carbon dioxide in the chloroplasts. In the presence of sunlight, this reaction produces sugar and oxygen. By means of this simple yet vital process, green plants restore oxygen to the atmosphere, feed themselves, and in turn feed all other forms of life.

With the approach of autumn, as the amount of daylight shortens, an abscission layer forms at the base of the leaves. This is the layer at which the leaves actually separate from the twigs. At the same time, chlorophyll is no longer being produced, possibly because the abscission layer gradually cuts off nutrients to the leaves. As the chlorophyll breaks down, the leaves begin to turn yellow and orange as a result of xanthophylls and carotenes present in the leaves, previously masked by the chlorophyll. When all nutrients to the leaves are cut off, the abscission layer separates and the leaves fall. A leaf scar forms just below the bud formed during the summer. That bud becomes next year's leaf.

1—1. Oak in cross section: (A) cambium; (B) inner bark; (C) outer bark; (D) sapwood; (E) heartwood; (F) pith; (G) rays.

WOOD STRUCTURE

Wood, or xylem, is the cellular material that makes up the bulk of the tree. It consists mainly of dead, hollow cells. Chemically, wood is composed of 40—50 percent cellulose, 20—35 percent hemicellulose, and 15—30 percent lignin. Cellulose is a very long, complex, molecular chain, which when broken down yields the simple sugar glucose. Hemicellulose, closely associated with cellulose, is composed of more than one type of sugar. Lignin is an intercellular material that bonds the wood fibers together. Aside from these three major components, various extractives are also present in the wood. Although not part of the wood structure, these extractives are usually located in the cell cavities, or lumens, and contribute to the wood's characteristic color, odor, taste, decay resistence, and flammability. These secondary ingredients include oils, tannins, waxes and gums, starches, alkaloids, color materials, and about 1—2 percent ash-forming minerals such as calcium and silica.

Figure 1—1 shows a typical cross section of a hardwood stem. (A) is the cambium, a layer only one cell in thickness, which produces new bark (phloem) toward the outside of the tree and wood (xylem) toward the inside of the tree. Cambium extends in a continuous layer between the wood and the bark and gives rise to the tree's lateral growth. During the course of a year, one new ring of wood is added to the trunk, roots, and branches. Wood formed the previous year does not continue to grow. The width of the rings is not necessarily consistent in size, even within a species. Ash grown in areas of little rainfall and poor soil may have up to 40 rings per inch (2.5 centimeters) of diameter (slow growth), whereas the same species grown in an area of abundant moisture and nutrients may have only 4 or 5 rings per inch of diameter (fast growth). (B) is the newly formed inner bark, a soft fibrous material that carries food down from the leaves to all parts of the tree. During the growing season, the cambium layer and the inner bark are very soft and fragile. This means that logs cut during spring and early summer will have easily peeled bark, whereas those cut during the winter will usually retain

1–2. Number of Annual Rings in the Sapwood of Hardwoods

Catalpa	*Catalpa speciosa*	1–2
Black locust	*Robinia pseudoacacia*	2–3
Chestnut	*Castanea dentata*	3–4
Butternut	*Juglans cinerea*	5–6
Osage orange	*Maclura pomifera*	5–10
Sassafras	*Sassafras albidum*	7–8
Black cherry	*Prunus serotina*	10–12
Black walnut	*Juglans nigra*	10–20
Apple	*Malus pumila*	12–30
Beech	*Fagus grandifolia*	20–30
Sugar maple	*Acer saccharum*	30–40
Dogwood	*Cornus florida*	30–40
Basswood	*Tilia americana*	55–65
Sweet birch	*Betula lenta*	60–80
Sweet gum	*Liquidambar styraciflua*	65–75
Persimmon	*Diospyros virginiana*	100+

Source: Charles Sprague Sargent, *Manual of the Trees of North America.*

1–3. Pith in black walnut.

their bark. (C) is the dead, corky outer bark. As the diameter of the tree increases year by year, the bark becomes thicker and begins to crack. With age it usually becomes quite thick and furrowed, and sloughs off from the action of wind and weather.

The newly formed wood is the sapwood (D). It constitutes from only 1 or 2 to over 200 years' growth (in some conifers), depending on the species (see figure 1–2). Sapwood functions primarily to conduct water and minerals from the roots to the leaves. Most of the newly formed cells die in a short time. A few, the parenchyma cells, retain their protoplasm in the cell cavity and act as living food-storage cells. After a number of years, the sapwood loses its function and turns to heartwood, figure 1–1 (E). The last of the parenchyma cells die, leaving only the cell walls, which give the tree structural support. Extractives are deposited in the heartwood cells, giving the wood its distinctive color. Usually one new ring of sapwood is formed under the bark each year, and the oldest ring of sapwood in turn becomes heartwood. Sapwood, having no extractives (some of which are toxic to fungi), is not as decay resistant as the heartwood, and should not be used in conditions conducive to decay. Heartwood does contain extractives, which add to the mass of its cells, and increases the density of the wood somewhat. While sapwood and heartwood are structurally identical, sapwood contains more moisture and no extractives, and consequently shrinks more than heartwood.

The pith is located in the center of the tree, figure 1–1 (F). This is a soft, sometimes spongey material formed behind the apical meristem. In most species it is only slightly visible as a darker tube. In some trees, such as black walnut (figure 1–3), butternut, and sumac, it is quite pronounced. Surrounding the pith is an undistinct area known as juvenile, or pith, wood, characterized by wide growth rings (especially in conifers), low density and strength, and much greater longitudinal shrinkage.

Radiating from the pith outward are the rays, figure 1–1 (G). They extend to the cambium and are used in the lateral transport of nutrients through the sapwood. One theory states that rays restrain the wood and therefore reduce radial dimensional change.

Trees grown in temperate climates have a cycle of growth and dormancy that results in the appearance of annual rings. Typically, each spring as growth resumes the cambial layer produces an abundance of large, thin-walled cells. Spring is a time of mild temperatures, maximum daylight, and an abundance of rainfall. Consequently, cell growth is quick and profuse. This initial growth is known as early wood or spring wood. As the season progresses and day length decreases, the weather gets hotter and dryer and the growth slows down. Cell formations become smaller and thicker walled. These are the late wood or summer wood cells. Finally, during autumn, growth stops for the season. Since the late wood cells have thicker walls, that portion of the growth ring is more dense. This is most apparent in old weathered wood, which takes on a ridged appearance as the early wood erodes faster than the denser late wood.

CLASSIFICATION OF TREES

Botanically, trees are divided into two classes, gymnosperms and angiosperms. Commercially, woods are divided into softwoods and hardwoods, the softwoods referring to the gymnosperms, and the hardwoods referring to the angiosperms. The terms *softwood* and *hardwood* should not be taken literally, since not all softwoods are soft (yellow pine is about as hard as black walnut), nor are all hardwoods hard (as with basswood and cottonwood). Since these terms will continue to be used in the trade, the knowledgeable woodworker should recognize that they are used merely to distinguish the two groups, not define them.

Gymnosperms, characterized by exposed seeds, are the older of the two groups, and include all conifers, ferns, and even the ginko (commonly thought of as a hardwood because of its broad, deciduous leaves). Conifers are characterized by a single straight trunk, and needles or scales, which are retained all year (except for cypresses and larches). Needles, usually smaller than leaves, have a waxlike coating that prevents water loss during the long winter months. Thus adapted, the conifers are the dominant tree of the northern forest. In southern areas they show rapid growth, and their long straight stems lend themselves well to lumber production.

Coniferous wood is fairly simple in structure. It is composed predominantly (roughly 90 percent) of all-purpose tracheid cells, which are long, thin, and hollow. Although the cells are closed at both ends, liquids pass from one cell to the next through "pits" in the cell walls. Conifers also contain rays, but only about 5 percent in volume. Some of these woods also contain resin canals, which are large (visible), tubular passages that exude resin or pitch. These canals occur in the species of pine (*Pinus*), larch (*Larix*), spruce (*Picea*), and Douglas fir (*Pseudotsuga*). Conifers lack specialized vessels or pores. Consequently, the entire group is classified as having nonporous wood.

The angiosperms as a class are younger than the gymnosperms. They are characterized by seeds that grow in husks, shells, or fruits, as opposed to coniferous seeds which are exposed between the scales of cones. Trees in this group usually have trunks that branch and rebranch. Most of these trees in the temperate zones are deciduous, loosing their leaves each fall, except for some species like holly (*Ilex*), which retains its leaves through the winter.

On a cellular level, the angiosperms are more specialized than the gymnosperms. They contain more rays, about 20 percent by volume, and only about 25 percent of the wood consists of tracheid cells. These, like the tracheids in conifers, are long, thin cells with thick walls that give the tree support. Around 50 percent of the wood is composed of vessels, tubular open-ended cells. They have thin walls and large diameters, specifically made for the conduction of sap. When the vessels are exposed by cutting across the grain they are called *pores*. Wood with large vessels such as oak or chestnut is said to be *open pored*, or *open grained*. These vessels, when exposed on any surface, are readily visible by eye and can be felt by a fingernail across what appears to be a smooth surface. Since vessel sizes vary so widely between species, designations such as open grain and close grain are relative. What is more important is the arrangement of the vessels in the growth ring.

When the vessels (pores) are formed primarily in early wood, the wood is called *ring porous*. The vessels form a distinct band in the early wood (figure 1−4). Vessels, although present in late wood, are much smaller and fewer. Ring-porous woods include ash, hickory, chestnut, Osage orange, oaks, elm, sassafras, and black locust.

At the other extreme are the woods that are *diffuse porous* (figure 1−5), those with pores scattered evenly throughout the year's growth. The pores are all about equal in size, so the early wood and late wood are therefore indistinct. Maple, birch, dogwood, beech, holly, poplar, magnolia, hornbeam, sycamore, willow, and basswood are diffuse-porous woods.

Between these two groups are the

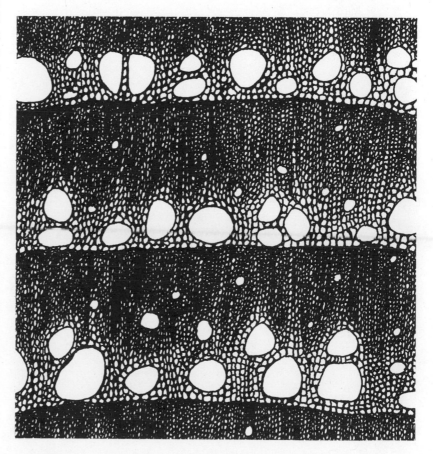

1−4. Ring-porous wood cross section (drawing: 30x ash).

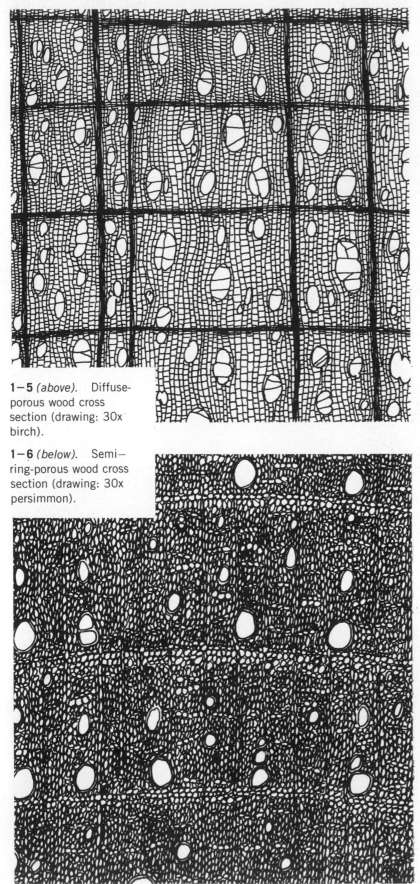

1—5 *(above).* Diffuse-porous wood cross section (drawing: 30x birch).

1—6 *(below).* Semi-ring-porous wood cross section (drawing: 30x persimmon).

semi—ring-porous (or *semi—diffuse-porous*) woods (figure 1—6). The main characteristic of these woods is a gradual change from large vessels in the early wood to small vessels in the late wood. Species that have typical semi—ring-porous wood include catalpa, persimmon, and plum. Certain species of hickory, walnut, oak, and willow are sometimes included in this group.

The pores of exposed end-grain heartwood will sometimes appear clogged with a frothy, filmlike substance called *tyloses*. Tyloses is formed in some species when the wood turns to heartwood. In woods such as red oak, cherry, maple, dogwood, honey locust, and sourwood, tyloses is insignificant or totally absent. In others such as white oak, tyloses development is quite extensive, while in Osage orange and black locust, the vessels are tightly filled.

WOOD PROPERTIES

Figure 1—7 shows the three faces or planes of wood. Cutting the tree parallel to the ground and perpendicular to the pith reveals the *cross section* or *transverse face*. Such a cut is in the transverse direction and shows the growth rings, pores, and rays.

Cutting in a plane parallel to and through the pith exposes the *radial face* and is in the radial direction. This cut reveals the parallel edges of the growth rings and best shows the widest portion of the rays.

Again cutting vertically through the trunk, parallel to but not through the pith, reveals the *tangential face* or plane, which displays the ends of the rays and the wide figure of the growth rings.

Wood is an anisotropic material: it has different and distinct properties in each of its three directions. In the longitudinal direction, with the length of the fibers, wood has its greatest shock resistance and compression strength. Hence the use of longitudinal lumber in posts, legs, and other members where weight and compression are a factor. In addition, wood shrinks an insignificant amount in this direction. Yet with all its compression strength, it splits in the radial and tangential direction. The rays form planes of weakness in the radial direction and allow splitting. In the transverse direction (cross section), wood refuses to split, yet compresses perpendicular to the grain. Compression is more severe on the tangential face than on the radial face. In ring-porous woods such as oak and ash, the concentration of large, thin-walled vessels in the early wood also forms rings of weakness. Utilizing this property, basketmakers beat ash logs to separate the growth rings, lifting them off in sheets.

COLOR AND LUSTER

Color in wood is caused by extractives in the heartwood. In most species the sapwood is a light, creamy tan color. Heartwood color varies tremendously among species, but within a species color is also variable. One theory states that the color depends on the type of soil in which the tree grew. Therefore, because of the variables, color should be used only secondarily as an aid to identification. Other factors also affect color: exposure to sunlight, which hastens the development of the patina; and finishes, which alter the natural darkening or bleaching process of the wood.

Although color is an unreliable factor in wood identification, it is this variability, in conjunction with the figure of the grain, that makes each piece of wood unique and adds to its aesthetic value.

Luster is the natural ability of wood to reflect light. It has nothing to do with the color or the finish of the wood. Luster is most apparent when the wood is planed with a sharp tool. This produces a smoother surface with more sheen than sanding, which abrades the wood and clogs the pores. Occasionally, luster can be used to identify wood. For instance, white ash has noticeably more luster than black ash.

TASTE AND ODOR

Extractives are also the cause of taste and odor in woods. Some are so distinctive they can be used in identification. Aromatic extractives are most noticeable in red and white cedar, black walnut, sugar pine, and sassafras. A few woods such as catalpa and tulip poplar have a rather disagreeable odor. Since many of the odor-causing extractives are volatile, they can be smelled only in green or freshly sawn wood. Taste is not usually pronounced in wood. Rather, woods are often chosen for their lack of taste. Butter tubs, cutting boards, and kitchen utensils are made of fir, spruce, maple, beech, and basswood for this reason.

SPECIFIC GRAVITY AND DENSITY

Specific gravity measures the relative amount of solid cell wall material; therefore, it is the best

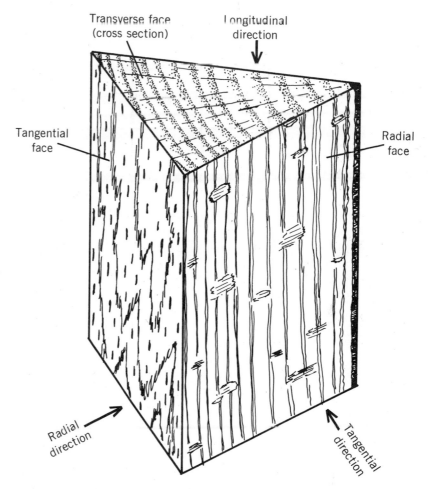

1-7. Three planes of wood: transverse; radial; and tangential.

index for predicting the strength of wood. It is expressed as the ratio of the weight of a substance (wood) compared to the weight of an equal volume of water. Therefore:

$$\text{specific gravity} = \frac{\text{ovendry weight of wood}}{\substack{\text{weight of displaced} \\ \text{volume of water}}}$$

The moisture content of the wood must always be specified, since the wetter the wood, the larger its volume and the more water it will displace. Therefore, the specific gravity will be higher the closer the wood is to its smallest (ovendry) volume. Conversely, as the wood swells it displaces more water, making the denominator of the ratio larger and the specific gravity smaller. Figure 1-8 lists the specific gravity of common woods at 12% (air dry) moisture content.

Water has a specific gravity of 1.0, whereas pure wood substance with no cell cavities would have a specific gravity of 1.46, almost 50% heavier than water. All wood however, has cell cavities filled with air or water.

1−8. SPECIFIC GRAVITY AND DENSITY

Species	Specific Gravity at 12% M.C.	Green	Density at 12% M.C. (g/cc)	(lbs./ft³)
Alder, red	.41	.37	.46	28
Ash, black	.49	.45	.55	34
white	.60	.55	.67	42
Bald cypress	.46	.42	.52	32
Basswood	.37	.32	.41	26
Beech	.64	.56	.71	45
Birch, paper	.55	.48	.61	38
yellow	.62	.55	.69	43
Butternut	.38	.36	.42	27
Catalpa	.41	.36	.46	29
Cedar, N. white	.31	.29	.34	22
red	.47	.44	.52	33
Cherry, black	.50	.42	.56	35
Chestnut, American	.43	.40	.48	30
Dogwood	.73	.64	.81	51
Elm, American	.50	.46	.56	35
Hickory, Shagbark	.72	.64	.80	50
Holly, American	.57	.50	.63	40
Honeylocust	.67	.60	.75	44
Hornbeam, American	.70	.58	.78	49
Locust, black	.69	.66	.77	48
Maple, red	.54	.49	.60	38
sugar	.63	.56	.70	44
Oak, N. red	.63	.56	.70	43
white	.68	.60	.76	45
Osage orange	.80	.76	.84	56
Pecan	.66	.60	.73	46
Persimmon	.74	.64	.78	52
Pine, sugar	.36	.34	.40	25
E. white	.35	.34	.39	25
Redwood	.40	.38	.43	20
Sassafras	.46	.42	.52	32
Sweet gum	.52	.46	.56	35
Sycamore	.49	.46	.54	34
Tulip poplar	.42	.40	.47	30
Walnut, black	.55	.51	.61	38

SOURCE: U.S. Forest Products Laboratory, *Wood Handbook: Wood as an Engineering Material,* U.S.D.A. Handbook No. 72.

Live oak has the highest specific gravity, .98 ovendry, of any North American wood. Other hard and heavy woods with an ovendry specific gravity above .70 are: Osage orange, .84; dogwood, .70−.80; persimmon, .79; hickory, .78; eastern hornbeam, .78; and black locust, .73.[1] The specific gravity of native conifers (softwoods) ranges from .29 to .55 at 12% moisture content, while that of the native deciduous

species (hardwoods) ranges from .31 to .88 at 12% moisture content.

Density is defined as mass per unit volume and is usually expressed as pounds/cubic foot (lb/ft³) or as grams/cubic centimenter (g/cc). Density also varies with the moisture content of the wood. Water weighs 62.4 lb/ft³ or 1 g/cc, so wood with a specific gravity of .50 (at 0% moisture) would weigh 31.2 lb/ft³ or .5 g/cc. Note that at 0% moisture content, specific gravity equals g/cc. A block of solid wood material at 0% moisture content, with no cell cavities, having a specific gravity of 1.46, would weigh 91.1 lb/ft³ or 1.46 g/cc. Density is a good indicator of hardness and the amount of shrinkage and swelling to be expected from a given species. The denser the wood, the more movement can be expected.

Density is easy to approximate by floating a long, thin, piece of wood upright in water. The ratio of the length below the water to the total length, times the weight of water per cubic foot, yields the density at that moisture content. For example, if a 14-inch (35.5 cm) stick is floated upright and 8.5 inches (21.6 cm) is below the water line, then

$$\frac{8.5}{14} \times 62.4 \text{ lb/ft}^3 = 37.9 \text{ lb/ft}^3$$

or

$$\frac{21.5}{35.5} \times 1 \text{ g/cc} = .61 \text{ g/cc}.$$

GRAIN AND FIGURE

A knowledge of the basic makeup of wood helps in the understanding of grain structure. Grain is simply the alignment of the wood cells. The term is also used in describing the arrangement, direction, size, and appearance of the fibers, vessels, and rays. Strictly speaking, figure is the appearance of the grain as it is exposed on the face of a board. In the lumber industry, figured wood refers to only certain types of irregular grain patterns. By simply splitting a piece of wood, one can determine whether the grain is straight or wavy. Wood from around branches, roots, and crotches will be wavy, wild, and extremely unpredictable and difficult to work.

In some trees the grain does not grow in a perfect vertical direction, but rather tends to twist around the trunk. This spiral growth is present to such an extent in both conifers and deciduous trees that, unless the spiral is severe, it is considered normal. In some species the

[1]Alexis J. Panshin and Carl de Zeeuw, *Textbook of Wood Technology*, pp. 537−628.

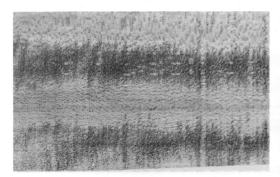

1—9 *(top left).* Interlocking grain looks fuzzy on sawn sycamore.

1—10 *(top right).* Split tiger-stripe maple (an abnormality of sugar maple) shows the undulating grain.

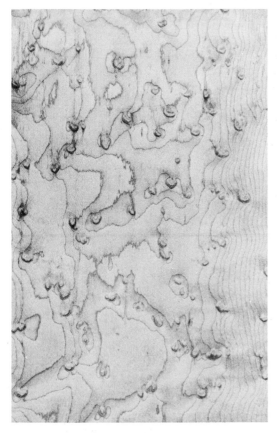

1—11 *(bottom left).* Bird's eye maple (abnormality of sugar maple).

1—12 *(bottom right).* Feather figure in white ash.

spiral reverses itself every few years, growing first in a clockwise spiral, then in a counter-clockwise spiral around the trunk. This is known as interlocking grain. It is a very difficult type of wood to split, chisel, or plane. The grain actually goes in opposite directions, and consequently reflects light in such a way as to appear striped. When sawn, the wood alternates between smooth and fuzzy areas, (figure 1—9). Interlocking grain is found in sycamore, elm, and black tupelo. Finished, it is sometimes known as ribbon grain because of the dark and light stripes.

Wavy grain patterns are a result of longitudinal cell growth in waves, resulting in a washboard appearance when the wood is split (figure 1—10). This occurs most often in birches and maples, and to some extent in ash and cherry. In maple, when the waves are small and tightly spaced, the grain is called tiger stripe or fiddleback. This abrupt oscillation of the grain results in dark and light areas, depending on the direction of the view.

Very rarely, areas of interconnecting ovals or grooves will form blister grain, or quilting, in maple. A more common figure is bird's eye (figure 1—11). This is caused by small indentations in the grain, more or less like dimples, usually evident under the inner bark. Since the cambium layer is the source of new growth, the bird's eye figure continues as each new ring is formed. Bird's eye varies in size and distribution. This figure, most common in rock maple (sugar maple), is also found in ash and birch.

There is no satisfactory explanation as to what exactly causes bird's eye or even tiger stripe. One of the most commonly accepted theories is that these figure variations result from stunted growth. They occur most often in trees on northeast slopes receiving a minimum of light. Recent research points to virus as a possible cause.

Crotch grain, or feathering around root and branch crotches, is caused by distortion of the grain and crowding and twisting of the annual growth. Feathering is one of the most common figures encountered. It occurs in almost all walnut and most ash trees (figure 1–12), less frequently in oak, birch, cherry, and to some extent in almost all hardwoods.

Another specialized pattern is pigment figure. Actually, it is not a type of figure at all, but rather streaks of color independent of the growth rings. Pigment figure is caused by uneven extractive deposits in the heartwood. An excess of dark deposits is most dramatic, but occasionally a lack of extractives may cause a lighter area in the heartwood known as false or included sapwood (see figure 2–6). Pigment figure is common in black walnut, eastern red cedar, and sweet gum, and is sometimes present in cherry and even pine.

DEFECTS AND ABNORMALITIES

Wood, being an organic material, varies in character and properties. These variations can be either detrimental or beneficial from the woodworker's point of view.

WARP
Warped wood is by far the most common complaint (figure 1–13). Warps are usually categorized as *cups* (curvature from the wide face of the board to the other); *bows* (curvature from one end of the board to the other with ends remaining straight); *crooks* (curvature from one end to the other with the faces remaining flat); and *twists* (airplane propellers). These dimensional changes are usually a result of uneven shrinkage. Cupping, for example, is caused by the faces of a board drying at different rates. It is also caused by the difference in radial and tangential shrinkage. On a plainsawn board, this difference is usually manifested in the concave surface forming away from the center of the tree. It is most pronounced in flat sawn lumber.

Case hardening is another cause of warpage. It usually occurs in kiln-dried lumber, when the wood is dried too fast or is not "conditioned" prior to removal from the kiln. Drying wood too fast creates stresses. The outside (shell) dries and begins to shrink, while the inside (core) is still wet. Thus the surface wood is stretched and is under tension, compressing the core. The outer fibers dry in the tension state, whereas the inner fibers eventually dry in the compressed state. This condition is not apparent until the board is worked, either planed unevenly or resawn. Then the internal stresses result in warp, usually a cup.

Severe warping is also caused by reaction wood (see p. 13).

Warps should not always be considered defects. In some cases woodworkers can use warps to their advantage. For instance, when a curve is needed on a high-post bed canopy, a severely bowed board cut into strips is ideal. These will then form a gentle crown, as opposed to straight stock, which would have a tendency to sag.

STAIN
Stain in wood can be caused by one of several factors. Blue stain, probably the most prevalent, is brought about by a fungus and is a direct result of poor air circulation. Freshly sawn or partially dried wood is most susceptible and must be stickered immediately with small strips

1–13. Warps: (A) cup; (B) bow; (C) crook; (D) twist.

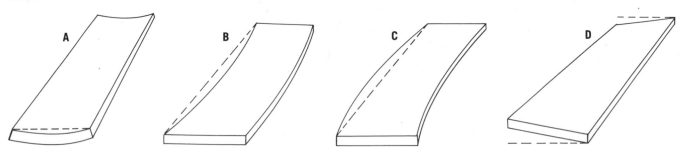

or stickers placed between the boards to allow air circulation. Brown stain is the result of a chemical reaction (oxidation) often occurring in the sapwood. Water-soluble chemicals are brought to the surface and deposited there as the water evaporates. Kiln dried softwoods are prone to brown stain if kiln temperatures exceed 130°F (54°C).

Sticker stain results from the use of damp stickers. The stain itself is caused by extractive accumulation or fungal growth between the freshly cut board and the damp sticker.

Woods containing tannins, such as oak and chestnut, will stain in the prolonged presence of iron. Not only are buried fence nails a headache for sawyers, they also leave long stains in the wood above and below the nail. Often the nail will have totally dissolved from the tannic acid, leaving only a long, bluish-black stain in the wood.

SPALTING

Spalting (or incipient decay) is an early step in the decay process. Associated with white rot, spalting forms distinctive zones of white, tan, pink, and brown, outlined in black (figure 1–14). These zones are actually areas that have been invaded by fungi, different fungi producing different colors. Spalting occurs in wood left in contact with soil or water (but not submerged). It is most often found in birch, maple, and beech and other non-decay-resistant woods. The most dramatic spalting, by far, occurs in sugar maple. To some woodworkers it is a desirable visual asset, even though the wood becomes soft and spongy, making it difficult to work.

DECAY

After staining and spalting, decay sets in as fungi break down entire sections of wood fiber. The wood becomes soft and punky, loses its structure, and begins to crumble. Decay fungi require four basic things, the lack of any one of which can prevent its growth. Food is first. Fungus usually attacks the sapwood first, since the sapwood contains carbohydrates and no extractives, which are decay inhibitors in some species of wood. Water is also necessary for fungal growth; perfectly dry wood will not decay. (Dry rot is a misnomer.) Wooden objects found in Egyptian tombs, for instance, are as solid today as when they were built thousands of years ago. Wood does not have to be in direct contact with water to decay; damp air with little

1–14. Spalted wood, or incipient decay.

circulation will suffice. Temperature is another requirement. Fungal activity ceases below 40°F (5°C) and above 105°F (41°C). Therefore, decay or even staining is not usually a problem in winter. Finally, oxygen is necessary to the decay process. Wood kept totally submerged in water will not rot.

BARK, PITCH, AND GUM POCKETS

Injuries to a tree take several years to heal, depending on their severity. If the cambium layer is injured or removed in spots, it will cause a localized interruption of the growth ring. Every year the cambium on each side will advance a small amount in order to cover the injury. Bark is also produced. As the years progress, the growth begins to cover the injury from both sides, trapping the bark between the two sides. Within a few more years, the cambium will fuse again and form a continuous growth ring, leaving a small pocket of enclosed bark.

In softwoods with resin canals, injuries will cause resin (or pitch) to collect in pockets. These can form under the cambium and will then be covered with new growth the following year. When the wood is machined, the pockets will exude pitch. Pitch will stay in liquid form for years. In very old wood, the pitch crystallizes.

In some hardwoods, gums and extractives

1–15. Gum pockets in black cherry, usually located between the growth rings.

will sometimes collect in small pockets between the growth rings. This results in dark patches on the tangential surface (figure 1–15), or dark streaks on the radial surface. These gum pockets are a result of cell separations or even cell wall disintegration (gummosis). This is most prevalent in black cherry and sweetgum.

BRASHNESS

Certain types of wood will break with no warning, under lighter than expected load conditions. Brashness is the cause. Brash wood will break cleanly across the grain, with no long splinters or cracks (figure 1–16). It is usually much lighter in weight, up to 15 percent less than normal wood of the same species (although in some cases, brashness occurs in wood of normal or higher density). The light weight is the result of much thinner cell walls. In cross section, the annual rings can be either very narrow or very wide. The weakness is a result not

only of the thin cell walls, but in some cases a decrease in the cellulose content of the cell walls. The basic cause can be one of several factors: compression wood, excessive heat, or decay. When working with structural members such as table legs or chair parts, take care to avoid brash wood. This can be done by comparing relative weights or flexing the individual pieces.

BURLS

Burls are abnormal, cancerlike growth on trunks and branches, caused by viruses or gall-forming insects. The grain in burls twists and circles in all directions (figure 1–17). Often it contains heartwood and sapwood mixtures, bark and gum pockets, and pin knot formations. Structurally, it is quite unpredictable and is used predominantly in veneer and inlay work. Large burls can be used in bowl turnings because the wood shrinks more or less equally in all directions, unlike normal wood, which turns round objects oval upon drying.

1–16 *(left).* Brashness in a white ash spindle, left. Normal break in spindle, right.

1–17 *(top right).* Cross section of a burl in black cherry.

1–18 *(bottom right).* Reaction wood in pine. The darker, wider rings at the bottom are compression wood.

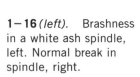

REACTION WOOD

Reaction wood is truly abnormal in its properties. It occurs in the timbers of leaning trees and in branches. It is usually indicated by eccentric annual growth rings, especially in conifers. The actual reaction wood is located in the side of greater growth. Reaction wood is the result of a growth response, to restore a leaning tree to an upright position or to maintain branch angles. It is believed that there is an asymmetrical response to growth hormones in those parts of the tree containing reaction wood.

In conifers, reaction wood is classified as *compression wood* and occurs on the lower side of the leaning stem. This is presumably because gravity seems to create compression on the lower side. It is readily apparent in cross section, visible as large annual rings and an inordinate amount of latewood (figure 1−18). The specific gravity is higher since the cell walls are much thicker, and the whole section appears darker. This is sometimes known by its German name, *rotholz*, or red wood. Even though the wood is denser and harder, it is also more brittle, because of the decreased amount of cellulose and increased amount of lignin present. Longitudinal shrinkage is about ten times as great as in normal wood. Across the grain it is somewhat less than normal, however. This causes severe warping problems.

Reaction wood in hardwoods is known as *tension wood* and usually forms on the upper side of the leaning stem. Tension wood occurs more commonly than is generally realized and is more difficult to detect than compression wood. The pith, for example, is not always located off center. One property of tension wood is that it is very fuzzy when sawn green. A certain amount of this fuzziness remains after drying, even after careful sanding, and this makes finishing (and especially staining) difficult. Like compression wood it has a greater longitudinal shrinkage, making it prone to warping. Tension wood has more cellulose and less lignin, which makes the wood stronger but more difficult to work.

CHAPTER 2

WOOD AND TREE IDENTIFICATION AND CHARACTERISTICS

A woodworker should have a rudimentary knowledge of the material available. Understanding wood and its characteristics—the trees, their leaves, branch structure, and bark—leads to a deeper appreciation of the wood itself.

This book is limited to the trees of North America. The selection of timbers on this continent is vast and varied. It takes years to become really familiar with all the working properties of even a few species. The range of textures and weights, colors and grain patterns is enough to satisfy any purpose. The secret lies in using the right wood for the right design. Each wood should be explored, used, tested, and evaluated. Local woods are relatively cheap, readily available, and can be suited to the intended use. It is far better to use material at hand, and use it well, than to import exotic woods with no knowledge of their working properties.

Except for the leaves of poison sumac (*Rhus vernix*), which cause dermatitis, and perhaps the dust of redwood (*Sequoia sempervirens*) and red cedar (*Juniperus virginiana*), which can cause allergic reactions in some persons, North American woods are generally considered safe.

Of the thirty woods listed in this chapter, about half are well known to most cabinetmakers. They are the popular commercial woods and should be available at well-stocked lumberyards or mills. The remaining species are not usually available commercially. Some do not grow in sufficient quantity and others do not grow to sufficient size to be harvested for the mass market. Yet these are marvelous timbers, beautifully colored and with a wide range of uses and working qualities. They, and others like them, are underutilized. What could be more appealing than a custom-made side table, wall cabinet, or stool of sycamore, sassafras, or persimmon? If the tree was cut locally, or even on one's own land, the wood seems all the more special. These woods should be tried and used. Often, they are available for a fraction of the cost of the more popular hardwoods.

This section is intended as a reference, a guide to the more common trees that can be easily identified by their shape, leaves, twigs, and bark. For others, such as the ashes and oaks, a more comprehensive manual is recommended to delineate the individual species (see Bibliography).

The silhouettes illustrated indicate each tree as an open-growth specimen, field grown under ideal light conditions. This basic shape is genetically programmed in the seed. The same tree grown under forest conditions may be quite different; it will probably have 40 feet (12 m) of clear trunk and a few spindly branches fighting for sunlight in the forest canopy. The forest-grown shape is environmentally induced by shade and the competition of surrounding trees. By using other characteristics, both shapes should be recognizable as the same species. The trees are listed by families, in the generally recognized progression from simple to complex plant structure.

EASTERN WHITE PINE
(Pinus strobus)

2—1. White pine, *Pinus strobus,* grows to 100 feet (30 m). (End-grain cross section, courtesy Ripon Microslides)

Eastern white pine is also referred to as northern, soft, balsam, or Weymouth pine. The Latin name *Pinus* refers to the pine family, while *strobus* means cone. The white pine's natural range is from Newfoundland to Manitoba, south to Wisconsin and Iowa, and east to Pennsylvania and New Jersey, extending down the Appalachians into northern Georgia. Ordinarily it reaches heights of 80—100 feet (24—30 m). The old king's broad arrow pines, used for masts in the royal navy, grew from 200 to 250 feet (60—75 m). It can grow to 400 years of age.

Pines, like most conifers, grow a straight central trunk. The branches usually grow horizontally in groups of five. The pine-shoot borer, an increasing pest in white pint planta-

Cone (¾ actual size)

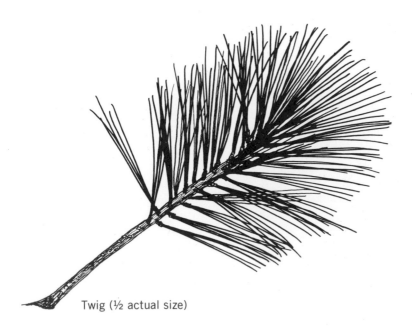

Twig (½ actual size)

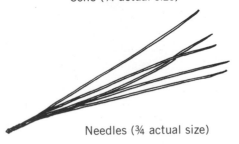

Needles (¾ actual size)

Bark

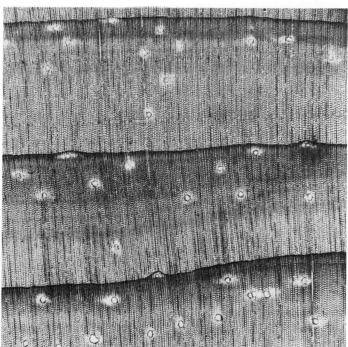

EASTERN WHITE PINE
(Pinus strobus)

End-grain cross section (15x)

tions, kills the leader stem, forcing one of the branches to take over as a new leader and resulting in a deformed trunk. Pine needles are 2–5 inches (5–12.5 cm) long, grow in bundles of five, and are surrounded by a papery sheath at the base which drops off during the first season. The needles themselves remain on the tree from one to three years. White pine cones are about 4–8 inches (10–20 cm) long, fairly thin, quite flexible, and take two years to mature. The bark forms gray, scaly ridges.

Sapwood of white pine is a pale yellow-white. Heartwood is cream to light reddish brown when freshly sawn, turning to a warm reddish brown on exposure to air and light. Old, clear heartwood is often referred to as pumpkin pine. Compared to other resinous species, white pine has very little pitch. It is generally straight, even grained, and light, with a density of 25 lb/ft³ or .39 g/cc at 12% moisture content (M.C.). It is a real workhorse in most shops, being used for jigs, braces, and mock-ups. As a pattern wood it has no equal. Its ease of sanding, chiseling, and planing makes it an ideal secondary wood. When used as such it fills the entire interior of a chest or wardrobe with a faint, clean, woody odor for years. Often it is used as a primary wood. Most of the New England painted antiques are constructed of

white pine. Shellac over the knots prevents the pitch from bleeding through. Perhaps it appears at its best when left raw or oiled to age naturally.

Face grain

SUGAR PINE
(*Pinus lambertiana*)

Sugar pine is also known as purple cone pine or big pine. Its Latin name refers to Dr. Aylmer Lambert, a British botanist. Because of its size, it is one of the most prolific producers of timber. The tallest of the pines, it commonly reaches heights of 160−180 feet (48−54 m) and diameters of 4−7 feet (1.2−2.1 m), and lives 300−500 years. Its natural range is from Oregon through California, at elevations of 1,000−2,000 feet (300−600 m) along the coast and 6,500−9,000 feet (2,000−2,750 m) inland. Sugar pines prefer loose, well-drained sandy loams, and grow best in areas having over 40 inches (100 cm) of annual precipitation.

Like the eastern white pine, the sugar pine also has 5 needles per bundle. They are 2½−4 inches (6.3−10 cm) long, bluish green in color, and remain on the tree for three years.

2−2. Sugar pine *Pinus lambertiana,* reaches 160−180 feet (49−55 m). (Bark photo, courtesy U.S. Forest Service; end-grain cross section, courtesy Ripon Microslides)

Twig (½ actual size)

Needles (actual size)

Cone (¼ actual size)

Bark

SUGAR PINE
(Pinus lambertiana)

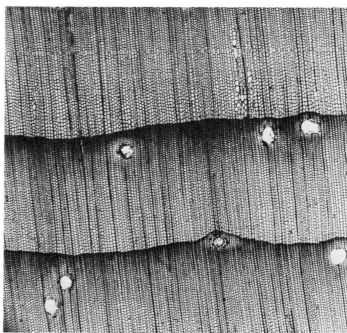

End-grain cross section (15x)

Face grain

The cones are purplish and erect when immature, shifting to a hanging position as they ripen the second year. They are 12–20 inches (30–50 cm) long, making them the largest of all pine cones. Sugar pine bark is deeply and irregularly grooved, with scaly cinnamon-brown ridges.

The sapwood is pale, while the heartwood is a light beige-yellow with prominent dark streaks. These are resin canals filled with crystallized resin. Sugar pine has a distinctly sweet odor resulting from the fresh or dried resin (pitch). The aged wood does not darken into a reddish orange like white pine, but turns to a light brown. With a density of about 25 lbs/ft³ or .39 g/cc at 12% M.C., the two woods are very similar in working qualities, although sugar pine is slightly coarser. It is used extensively in general millwork for sash, doors, and all types of trim and molding, as well as foundry patterns, building construction, signs, plywood, crates, and even organ pipes. It is not very decay resistant and should not be used in contact with soil or weather unless suitably treated. The wide, clear widths available make it an ideal cabinet wood.

REDWOOD
(Sequoia sempervirens)

The redwoods are the largest trees on this continent. Most trees cut commercially are 200–275 feet (61–83 m) tall and are 400–800 years old. The tallest measured tree is 359 feet (110 m). Trees of this size are over 2,000 years old. *Sequoia* is named in honor of the Cherokee Indian chief, and *sempervirens* means ever-living. The species is also known as California redwood or coastal redwood. Before the ice age, member of the redwood families covered much of North America. Today, only the redwood and the giant sequoia survive in a limited area, about 40 miles (64 km) wide and 500 miles (805 km) long, along the Pacific coast.

Redwood needles are flat and yellow

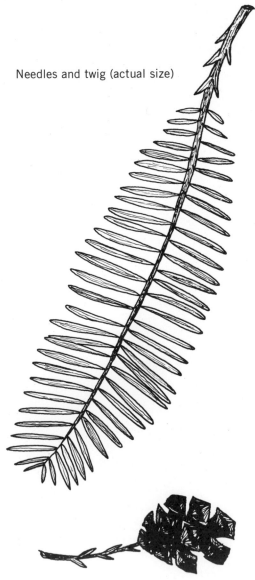

Needles and twig (actual size)

Cone (actual size)

2–3. Redwood, *Sequoia sempervirens,* grows to 200–275 feet (61–85 m), the tallest North American tree. (Bark photo, courtesy Alexander Disdier; end-grain cross section, courtesy Ripon Microslides)

Bark

REDWOOD
(Sequoia sempervirens)

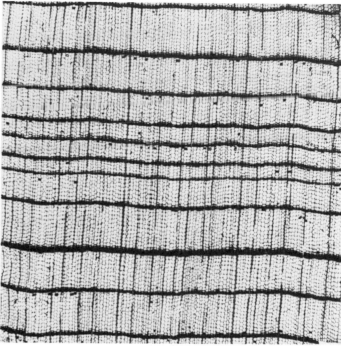

End-grain cross section (15x)

Face grain

green, especially on the twigs of young trees and the lower branches of older trees. On the main branches, they are small and scalelike. The cones are relatively small and purplish brown in color. Redwood bark on older trees can be up to 1 foot (30 cm) thick and is very resistant to fire. It is reddish gray, fibrous, and fluted.

Redwood has narrow, light, creamy sapwood and deep reddish brown heartwood. There are no resin canals, but rays are quite pronounced, especially on the radial surfaces. The grain is usually straight but coarse, appearing almost porous because of the large tracheids, which are easily visible with a hand lens. It is very light in weight, with a density of around 25 lbs/ft³ or .39 g/cc at 12% M.C. Redwood is closely related to the cedars, but lacks their odor or oily feel. Trees cut commercially can be 3−10 feet (.9−3 m) in diameter. The large size as well as its durability and decay resistance make it an ideal wood for building construction. It is widely used for sills, joists, posts, interior and exterior siding, doors, sash, tanks, and vats. Other outdoor uses include stadium seats, boat building, outdoor furniture, decks, shingles, and shakes. The wood is used only occasionally for cabinet work, although the root burls are used frequently for veneer and slab tables.

BALD CYPRESS
(Taxodium distichum)

2–4. Bald cypress, *Taxodium distichum,* grows 100–125 feet (30–38 m). (End-grain cross section, courtesy Ripon Microslides)

The Latin *Taxodium* comes from the Greek, meaning like a yew, while *distichum* means two-ranked and refers to the rows of needles on either side of the twig. In various parts of the South, the bald cypress is known as white, yellow, red (depending on the wood color), southern, or Gulf cypress. Its natural range is along the southeastern coastal states, from Delaware to Texas, as well as up the Mississippi basin to Indiana and Illinois. The species prefers moist, low, swampy areas. Under ideal conditions trees can reach 100–125 feet (30–37.5 m) in height. The trunk usually has an extremely flared base, around which knees, or knobby protruding roots, form in particularly wet areas.

The bald cypress is an oddity amongst conifers in that it is not an evergreen. Its light-green needles turn yellow and shed each fall. Cypress cones are 1-inch (2.5-cm) spheres composed of small rhomboid scales. The bark is reddish brown, fibrous, and tends to peel off on older trees. Young trees grow with a straight trunk and pyramidal shape, but the crown tends to branch out and become irregular as the tree matures.

Cypress sapwood is light in color and merges gradually into the heartwood. It is one of the most variable woods as far as weight and color are concerned. Color ranges from straw yellow through brown, from reddish brown to almost black. The density seems to be related to the color, the darker wood being heavier. It averages around 32 lbs/ft³ or .52 g/cc at 12% M.C. The wood feels slightly oily, has a rancid

Needles (⅔ actual size)

Cone and twig (actual size)

BALD CYPRESS
(Taxodium distichum)

Bark

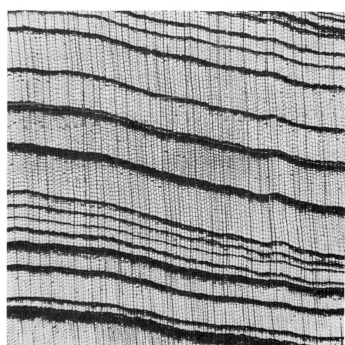

End-grain cross section (15x)

Face grain

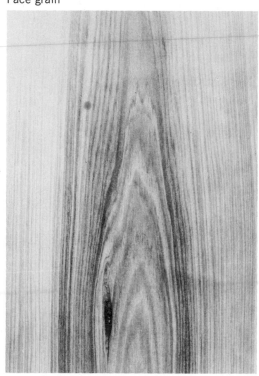

odor, and is coarse textured. Rays are quite conspicuous for a conifer. The heartwood is extremely decay resistant and is used extensively for siding, dock and bridge timbers, fence posts, and railroad ties. It is used for doors, sash, trim, paneling, boxes and crates, vats, and containers for corrosive chemicals. Outdoors it is used for tanks, silos, greenhouse frames, shipbuilding, decks, and garden furniture. Crotches and burls are sometimes cut for veneer.

NORTHERN WHITE CEDAR
(*Thuja occidentalis*)

Northern white cedar is known to most people as arborvitae. It is not a true cedar. Indians of the northeast referred to it as the feather-leaf tree or Oo-soo-ha-ta. It is found in swamps and forests from southern Labrador through southern Canada, into Manitoba, south to Wisconsin, and east to New York. It also extends down the Appalachians into Tennessee. Normally it reaches a height of 50–60 feet (15–18 m); however, in the southern part of its range, it is reduced to a small tree or shrub. White cedars form a natural pyramidal crown and are frequently used as ornamentals.

The foliage consists of flat, overlapping scales having a spicy odor. Oil of cedar is distilled from the twigs and leaves. The cones are very small, only ⅜ inch (1 cm) long, and grow in an upright position at the tips of the scaly twigs. They mature the first year and remain on the tree through the winter. Cedar bark is thin, reddish brown, and grows in fissures and interconnecting ridges that often appear shredded. In older trees the bark turns a grayish brown.

The wood is fine textured, even, and straight grained, has no resin canals, and very small rays. It has nearly white sapwood and a straw-colored heartwood, with a very pleasant odor. White cedar has a density of only 22 lbs/ft³ or .34 g/cc at 12% M.C., making it the lightest of any North American wood harvested commercially. One of its uses, therefore, is in fishnet floats and imitation minnows; its light weight and bouyancy also make it ideal for

2–5. Northern white cedar, *Thuja occidentalis,* grows to 50–60 feet (15–18 m). (End-grain cross section, courtesy Ripon Microslides)

Cone (actual size)

Needles (scales) and twig (actual size)

NORTHERN WHITE CEDAR
(Thuja occidentalis)

Bark

End-grain cross section (15x)

Face grain

canoe building. Because of its fragrance, it is useful in cabinet work as a secondary wood for drawer bottoms, linings, dividers, and backs. White cedar is also an extremely decay-resistant wood. Its largest commercial use is for shingles, which turn a silvery gray when exposed to the weather. Other uses are fence posts, rustic prefab log cabins, and slack cooperage.

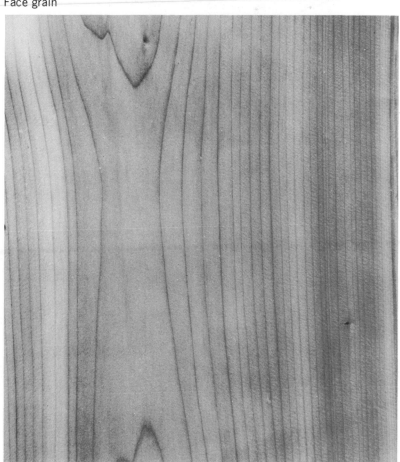

EASTERN RED CEDAR
(Juniperus virginiana)

2—6. Eastern red cedar, *Juniperus virginiana,* reaches 20—50 feet (6—15 m). (End-grain cross section, courtesy Ripon Microslides)

Red cedar belongs to the juniper family and is sometimes called red juniper. Under normal conditions it grows to a height of 20—50 feet (6—15 m), although in the southern portions of its range, growing in fertile soil, it can reach as much as 100 feet (30 m). Red cedar is a slow-growing tree and lives up to 200 years. Its natural range is from southern Maine to the Dakotas, south to Texas and east to northern Florida. Most often it is found growing in abandoned fields and along fence lines.

The needles of the red cedar are of two types. Young growth consists of small, sharp needles, whereas on older branches the needles appear compressed and scalelike. The fruits consist of small green berries that turn to a bluish purple when ripe. They are prized by gourmet cooks as a spice, by gin distillers, and by wildlife as a food source. The bark of the red cedar is thin, reddish brown, and shredded.

Red cedar has thin, light-colored sapwood.

Twig and needles — immature (actual size)

Needles and fruit — mature with fruit (actual size)

EASTERN RED CEDAR
(Juniperus virginiana)

Bark

End-grain cross section (15x)

Face grain

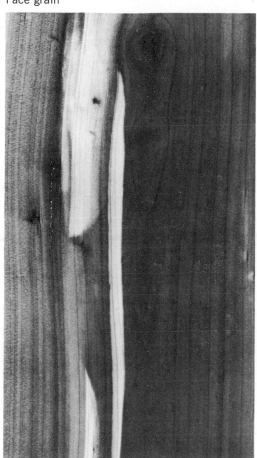

It is unique among the native conifers in that the heartwood is a bright reddish purple that ages to a reddish brown. The density is about 33 lbs/ft³ or .52 g/cc at 12% M.C. Although the wood is soft and works well with hand tools, it usually contains many knots. It is also noted for a high occurrence of included sapwood. Every gift shop in every tourist town has a collection of highly lacquered plaques with witty phrases; these novelty items are usually made of red cedar. The largest commercial use is in linings for closets and clothes chests because of the wood's aromatic, moth-repellant properties. Other uses include fence posts and pencils.

BLACK WALNUT
(*Juglans nigra*)

Black walnut is a member of the walnut family, which also includes butternut and the hickories. *Juglans* means nut of Jupiter, while *nigra*, black, refers to the dark wood. Its natural range is from New England through southern Ontario to South Dakota, south to Texas, and east to northern Florida. Walnut grows best in deep rich soils of river valleys and bottom lands, where it reaches a height of 60–100 feet (18–30 m). The tree itself generally has an open crown with thick sturdy branches.

Walnut leaves are compound, 1–2 feet (30–60 cm) long, with 13–23 lance-shaped leaflets. Leaves grow alternately on thick stubby twigs. When cut, the twigs reveal a light-brown pith, about the thickness of a pencil lead. Overall, the light-green foliage is scant, giving the tree an airy appearance. Early in the fall the leaves turn yellow and drop, leaving a distinctive 3-lobed notched leaf scar; at about the same time the nuts mature, enclosed in thick green pulpy husks that are about the size of a billiard ball. The deeply grooved black nut is very thick and hard, but the taste is worth the effort of extracting the meat. The dark-brown bark grows in broken ridges.

2–7. Black walnut, *Juglans nigra*, grows 60–100 feet tall (18–30 m). (End-grain cross section, courtesy Ripon Microslides)

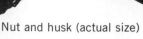

Nut and husk (actual size)

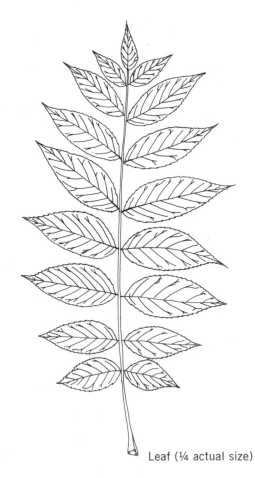

Twig with chambered pith (actual size)

Leaf (¼ actual size)

Bark

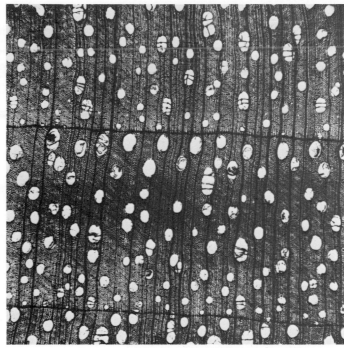
End-grain cross section (15x)

Face grain

Black walnut is as close to a perfect cabinet wood as can be found in North America. The light sapwood, 10–20 rings wide, is often steamed commercially to make it blend with the heartwood, which is a medium chocolate to purplish brown. The wood is medium hard (with a density of about 38 lbs/ft³ or .61 g/cc at 12% M.C.), strong, and works well with all hand and power tools, even the lathe. It has a pleasant odor when sawn or sanded. Classified as semi-ring porous, the pores (containing tyloses) are large enough to be seen on any surface. Walnut is extremely decay resistant and was once used for railroad ties. Many a barn and privy in the Appalachian region is constructed with a walnut frame. Its color, beauty, and workability make it the prime cabinet wood. Gunsmiths use it for stocks, since it moves very little once dried, therefore putting no pressure on the gun barrel. The biggest use today is for veneer. Top-quality butt logs will sell for thousands of dollars and will panel miles of executive offices.

BUTTERNUT
(*Juglans cinerea*)

2-8. Butternut, *Juglans cinerea*, grows 60-80 feet tall (18-24 m). (End-grain cross section, courtesy Ripon Microslides)

Butternut, the closest relative to black walnut, is sometimes known as white walnut, oilnut, or lemon walnut. It is a rather short, spreading tree, growing to only 30-50 feet (9-15 m) in the open and occasionally reaching 60-80 feet (18-24 m) in the forest. In pastures and along fence rows, the tree usually branches out a few feet above ground. The branches are subject to wind and snow damage, and the wood of the large trees is frequently unsound. The trees are short-lived, seldom becoming more than 75 years old. Their natural habitat extends from New Brunswick through southern Canada into Wisconsin, south to Missouri, and east to Virginia.

Several differences in leaf, branch, and fruit structure make the butternut distinguishable from the black walnut. Butternut has 11-17 light-green sticky leaflets on its compound leaves reaching a total of 15-30 inches (38-76 cm) in length. The twigs have a long terminal bud and a small downy pad between the lateral bud and the leaf scar of the previous year. The pith in the twig is dark brown. The nuts are green and oval in shape, almost like pecans. The bark is gray-brown and ridged.

Butternut has a light creamy sapwood under 1 inch (2.5 cm) wide. The heartwood is a medium chestnut brown and quite lustrous. It

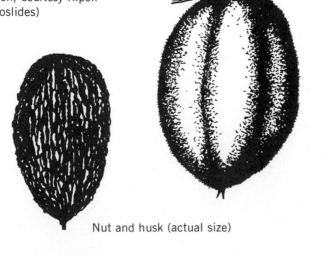

Nut and husk (actual size)

Twig with chambered pith (actual size)

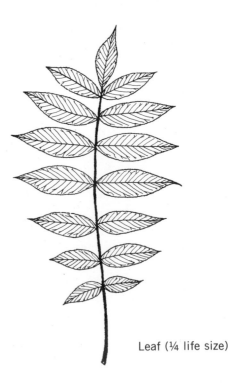

Leaf (¼ life size)

Bark

BUTTERNUT
(*Juglans cinerea*)

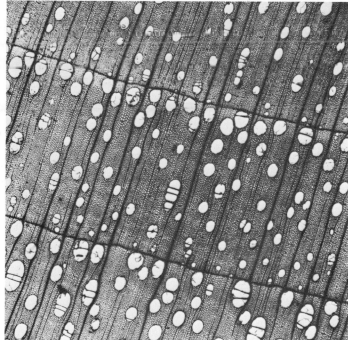

End-grain cross section (15x)

Face grain

is very soft and light in weight, having a density of about 27 lbs/ft³ or .42 g/cc at 12% M.C. The pores of this ring-porous wood are easily visible by eye and are filled with tyloses, while the rays are almost too small to be seen. The wood is used in fine cabinet work, paneling and interiors, veneer, toys, and for most millwork such as doors, sash, and trim. It tools and machines very well and is a pleasant wood to work with. Whereas most woods darken or bleach with age, butternut is one of the few that remains a medium brown in color.

SHAGBARK HICKORY
(*Carya ovata*)

2−9. Shagbark hickory, *Carya ovata*, grows to 140 feet (43 m). (End-grain cross section, courtesy Ripon Microslides)

Shagbark is also known as Carolina, shellbark, or upland hickory. *Carya* comes from the Greek for nut, while *ovata* is from the Latin meaning egg shaped, referring to the nut. The tree is tall and stately, often reaching heights of 120−140 feet (36−42 m), with trunk diameter of 20−30 inches (50−75 cm). The branches are often gnarled and crooked, giving an appearance of old age. Hickories will in fact reach 150−200 years of age. The shagbark hickory is a predominant species of the eastern forest, growing from New England through southern Canada to Iowa, south to Texas, and east to northern Florida.

As the name implies, the bark is unusually shaggy, forming long, thin silver-gray plates that are loose at both ends. The hickory nut is light brown, thin shelled, edible, and enclosed in a thick green 4-sectioned husk. The compound leaf consists of 5 (sometimes 7) leaflets attached directly to the stalk. Buds are alternate.

The woods of the various hickories are almost impossible to distinguish. Shagbark sapwood is light tan to pale brown and very thin; the heartwood is a pale reddish brown. It is very heavy and hard, with a density of 50 lbs/ft³ or .72 g/cc at 12% M.C. The ring-porous wood is extremely tough and elastic. No other commercial wood has comparable properties. These characteristics make it a prime wood for handles on impact tools such as axes, picks, and hammers. Wood with no more than 20 rings to the inch (slow-grown wood) is considered best. It was once the most important wood for the

Nut and husk (actual size)

Twig (actual size)

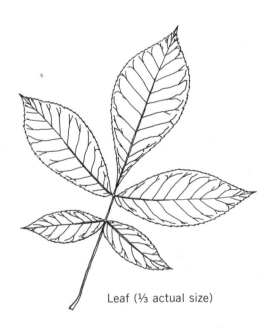

Leaf (⅓ actual size)

SHAGBARK HICKORY
(Carya ovata)

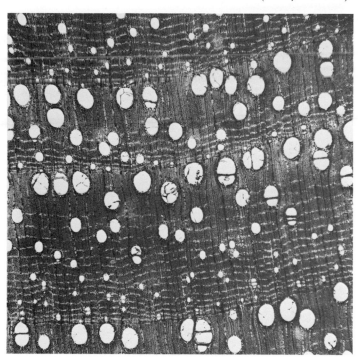

Bark

End-grain cross section (15x)

Face grain

wheelwright, used for spokes, axles, wheel rims, shafts, and even springs. Today it is the choice wood in athletic equipment such as skis and gymnastic bars. Its other uses include flooring, agricultural implements, and fuel for smoking meat. For chair construction it is unexcelled.

YELLOW BIRCH
(Betula allegheniensis)

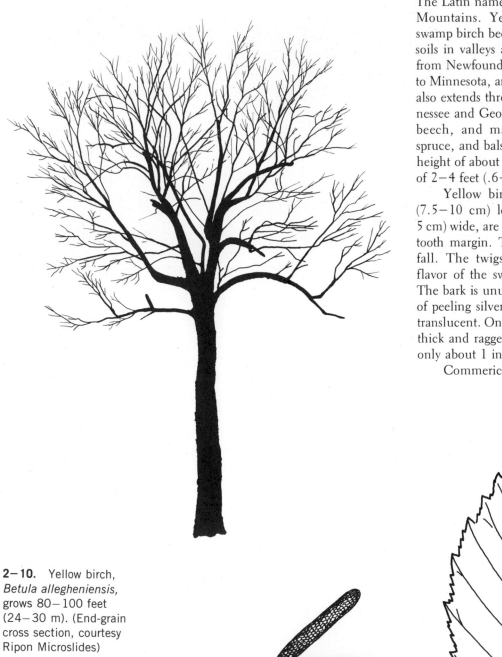

The Latin name means birch of the Allegheny Mountains. Yellow birch is also known as swamp birch because of its preference for moist soils in valleys and along streams. Its range is from Newfoundland through southern Canada to Minnesota, and southeast to Pennyslvania. It also extends through the Appalachians to Tennessee and Georgia. It grows with other birch, beech, and maple, as well as white pine, spruce, and balsam fir. Yellow birch reaches a height of about 100 feet (30 m) and a diameter of 2−4 feet (.6−1.2 m).

Yellow birch leaves, about 3−4 inches (7.5−10 cm) long and 1½−2 inches (3.8−5 cm) wide, are oval and pointed, with a double tooth margin. They turn bright yellow in the fall. The twigs lack the strong wintergreen flavor of the sweet birch. Buds are alternate. The bark is unusual in that it consists of layers of peeling silvery-yellow sheets that are almost translucent. On old trees the bark becomes quite thick and ragged. The small conelike fruit are only about 1 inch (1 cm) long.

Commerically, yellow birch is the most

2−10. Yellow birch, *Betula allegheniensis*, grows 80−100 feet (24−30 m). (End-grain cross section, courtesy Ripon Microslides)

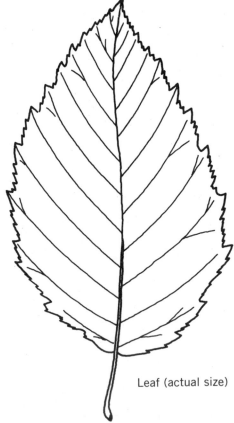

Twig (actual size)

Cone (actual size)

Leaf (actual size)

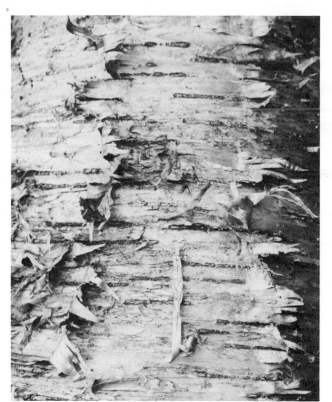

Bark

YELLOW BIRCH
(Betula allegheniensis)

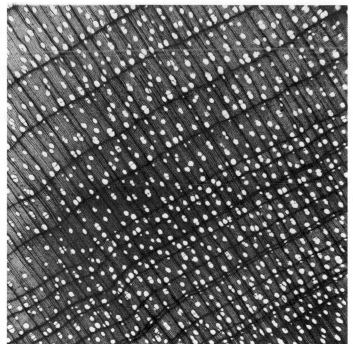

End-grain cross section (15x)

important and valuable of the birches. The sapwood is pale, and the heartwood is light to dark reddish brown, often heavily figured. It is moderately hard and heavy, with a density of 42 lbs/ft³ or .69 g/cc at 12% M.C. The wood is diffuse porous, with rays almost too small to be seen. It is difficult to distinguish between the birch species, although yellow and black birch are the heaviest. Yellow birch is used for veneer production, interior paneling, kitchen cabinets (stained "fruitwood"), and furniture. It is also used for flooring, toys, doors, sash, trim, butcher blocks, and toothpicks. Its availability, relatively low price, and good working quality make it an ideal wood for almost any type of cabinet work.

Face grain

BEECH
(Fagus grandifolia)

The beech tree is one of the few species that goes by one name in all parts of North America. The Latin name *Fagus* comes from the Greek, *phagus*, to eat, referring to the nuts. *Grandifolia* means large leaf. While the beech family includes the chestnuts and the oaks, the beech is the only native member of the genus *Fagus* in North America. The natural range is from Nova Scotia to Wisconsin, south to Louisiana, and east to Northern Florida. The largest specimens grow in the southern parts of the range, often reaching 120 feet (36 m) in height and up to 4 feet (1.2 m) in diameter. The tree has a large crown with gnarled, arthritic-looking branches that droop near the bottom, grow horizontally in the middle, and are up-right near the top.

The bark, even on old trees, is smooth and silvery gray, and seems particularly attractive to initial-carvers. Beech leaves are pointed, oblong ovals with serrated edges and parallel veins running from the central vein. In the fall the foliage turns yellow and bronze, often remaining on the tree until spring. The buds are long

2–11. Beech, *Fagus grandifolia*, reaches 80–120 feet (24–36 m). (End-grain cross section, courtesy Ripon Microslides)

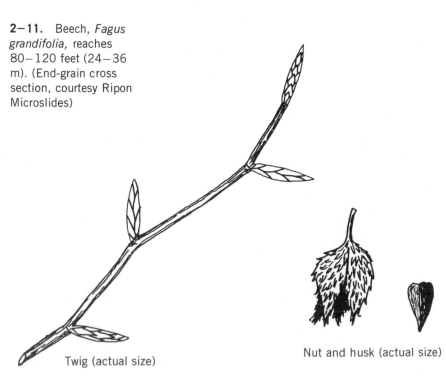

Twig (actual size)

Nut and husk (actual size)

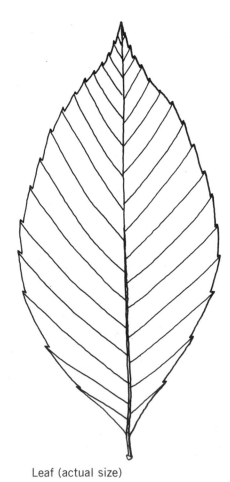

Leaf (actual size)

Bark

BEECH
(*Fagus grandifolia*)

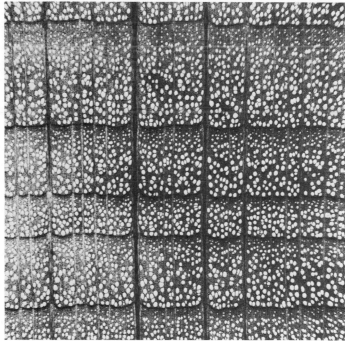

End-grain cross section (15x)

(⅜−1 inch or 1.5−2.5 cm) and pointed. The twigs angle away from the buds, giving a zigzag appearance. Beechnuts consist of two small triangular nuts, encased in one 4-sided burred husk.

Beech wood is diffuse porous and has a pinkish brown heartwood with numerous small but conspicuous rays. The sapwood is creamy white and 20−30 growth rings in width. With a density of 45 lbs/ft³ or .71 g/cc at 12% M.C., it makes a sturdy cabinet wood. Its two biggest faults are extreme shrinkage during drying (which usually starts immediately after being sawn) and total lack of decay resistance. Once dry, however, it moves very little and can be used for a multitude of purposes if not exposed to the weather. Most saw handles and kitchen utensils are made of beech wood, as are high-priced workbenches. Charcoal production, pulp, plywood, flooring, spools and clothes-pins, and kitchen cabinets are among its other uses. The wood bends well and is often used in steamed and bent chair parts.

Face grain

AMERICAN CHESTNUT
(*Castanea dentata*)

The American chestnut was perhaps one of the most versatile and best-loved trees. The blight *Endothia parasitica*, brought from Asia in 1904, swept through the eastern forests and by the end of the 1930s made chestnut virtually a memory. Sprouting stumps and isolated pockets of trees still persist. Researchers in France and the United States are at work on a hypovirulent strain of the fungus, which seems to hold promise for this once magnificent tree. *Castanea* is the classical name of the chestnut. *Dentata* means toothed, referring to the toothed leaf margin. The chestnut's natural range was from Maine through southern Canada to Indiana, Illinois, and Mississippi, east to Georgia, and up the east coast to Virginia. They grew to

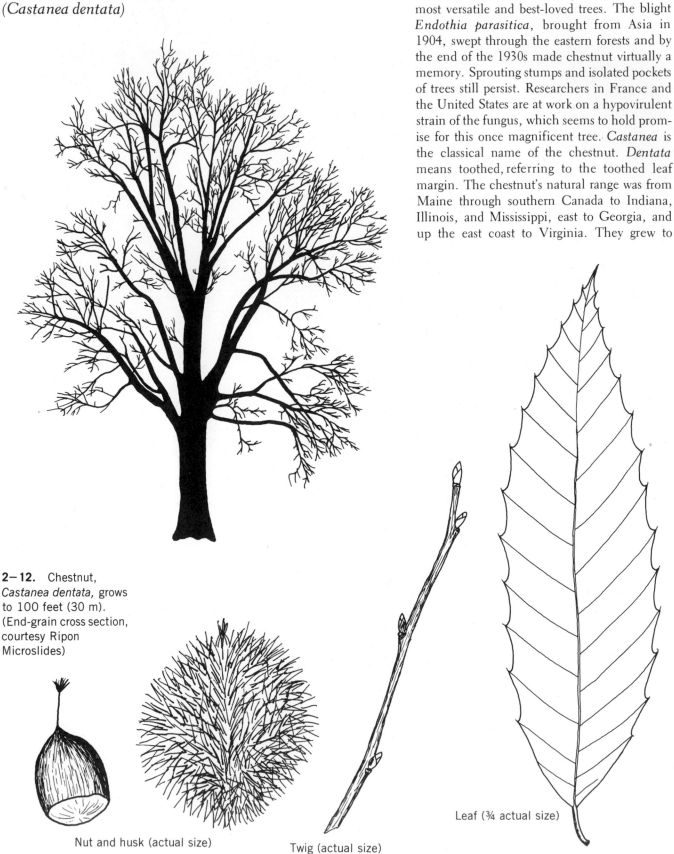

2–12. Chestnut, *Castanea dentata*, grows to 100 feet (30 m). (End-grain cross section, courtesy Ripon Microslides)

Nut and husk (actual size)

Twig (actual size)

Leaf (¾ actual size)

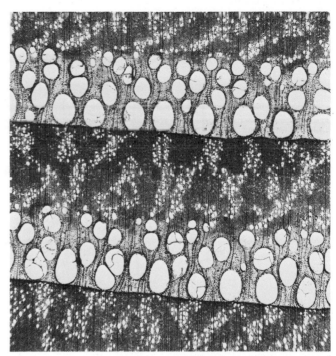

AMERICAN CHESTNUT
(Castanea dentata)

End-grain cross section (15x)

Bark

Face grain

heights of 80–100 feet (24–30 m), and 3–4 feet (.9–1.2 m) in diameter.

Chestnut leaves are 5–10 inches (12.5–25 cm) long, lance shaped, with prominent teeth along the edges. Long stringy male flowers and small clustered female flowers appear in June, and the tasty nuts, enclosed in prickly burrs, ripen in October. The bark on older trees is rough and gray, with deep, wide ridges. On younger trees it is smooth and often shiny. The buds are small and brown, growing alternately on thin purplish brown twigs.

Even though the blight killed most trees years ago, the wood is so decay resistant it is still being harvested from the silvery skeletons. Sapwood is narrow and light, and the ring-porous heartwood is a medium brown, darkening with age. It is straight grained, coarse, and moderately soft, with a density of 30 lbs/ft³ or .48 g/cc at 12% M.C. Chestnut was and is used for almost anything: construction timbers, split rail fences, posts, railroad ties, all aspects of cabinetry, millwork, and interior finishing. Because of the limited supply the wood is becoming more expensive.

RED OAK
(Quercus spp.)

Red oak is not a single species, but an entire group with similar characteristics, all members of the beech family. Species classified as red oak include northern red oak (*Q. rubra*), black oak (*Q. velutina*), southern red oak (*Q. falcata*), scarlet oak (*Q. coccinea*), pin oak (*Q. palustris*), Shumard oak (*Q. Shumardii*), and willow oak (*Q. phellos*). Red oaks range through most of the eastern and central United States, but only northern red oak grows into southern Canada. In open areas, red oaks grow into large, spreading trees with diameters of up to 6 feet (1.8 m).

The leaves of the entire group have sharp, pointed lobes, a characteristic distinguishing them from the rounded leaves of the white oaks. The leaves grow alternately on the twigs. The bark on most species is rough and dark gray to black. The acorns of all the red oaks take two years to mature.

Sapwood is narrow and light in color. Heartwood is pale pinkish brown and often smells like yeast when freshly cut. Red oak rays average ⅜–¾ inch (1–2 cm) high, rarely reaching more than an inch (2.5 cm). The ring-porous wood shows a gradual transition from early- to latewood. By far the surest

2–13. Northern red oak, *Quercus rubra,* grows 50–70 feet (15–21 m). (End-grain cross section, courtesy Ripon Microslides)

Twig (actual size)

Acorn (actual size)

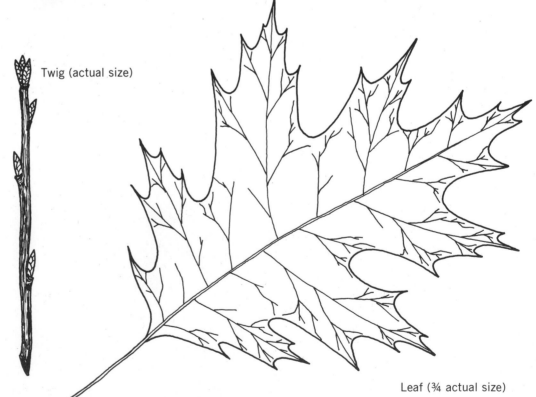

Leaf (¾ actual size)

RED OAK
(Quercus spp.)

Bark

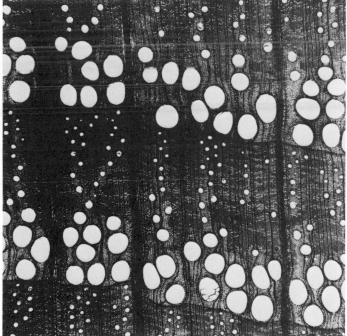

End-grain cross section (15x)

Face grain

method of distinguishing the red and white oaks is by the pores. Red oaks have fewer, larger, more rounded, and thicker-walled pores. Tyloses are seldom, if ever, present. Red oak is heavy and hard with a density of 43 lbs/ft³ or .70 g/cc at 12% M.C. It is not as decay resistant as white oak and is therefore used for a variety of indoor products such as flooring, veneer, furniture, kitchen cabinets, boxes, pallets, slack cooperage, handles, wainscotting, doors, sash, and trim. The wood planes and polishes well but tears on the lathe. Sharp edges should be avoided since they break under use and wear.

WHITE OAK
(*Quercus spp.*)

Quercus, the Latin name for the oaks, is derived from the Celtic meaning beautiful tree. The white oak group includes white oak (*Q. alba*), swamp white oak (*Q. bicolor*), bur oak (*Q. macrocarpa*), post oak (*Q. stellata*), overcup oak (*Q. lyrata*), chestnut oak (*Q. prinus*), swamp chestnut oak (*Q. michauxii*), and chinkapin oak (*Q. muehlenbergii*). Several local western species such as Oregon white oak, California white oak, gambrel oak, Arizona white oak, Mexican blue oak, and Emory oak are sometimes included. Most of the white oaks are eastern species, extending from Maine to Minnesota, south to Texas, and east to Florida. Bur oak even extends into southern Canada. White oaks obtain heights to 150 feet (45 m). Field-grown oaks will usually grow to only 80 feet (24 m) but will spread the same distance. They prefer moist fertile soil. Oaks grow very slowly; individual white oaks can reach 800 years of age.

Leaves of the white oaks have rounded lobes. The acorns take only one year to mature. Buds are small, rounded, and grow alternately

2-14. White oak, *Quercus alba,* grows 80-100 feet tall (24-30 m). (End-grain cross section, courtesy Ripon Microslides)

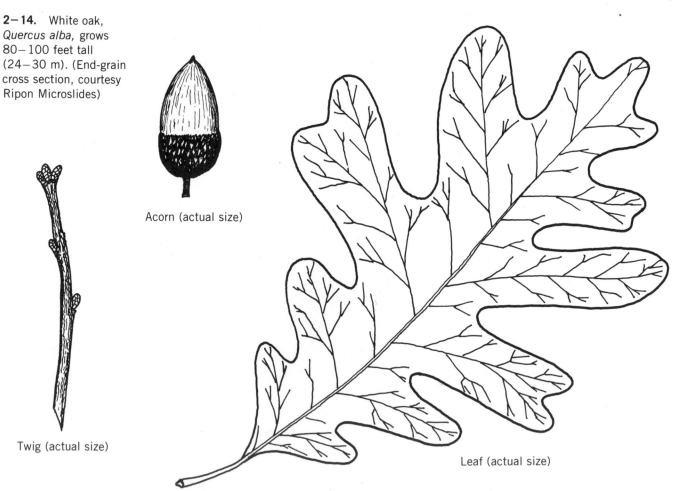

Twig (actual size)

Acorn (actual size)

Leaf (actual size)

Bark

WHITE OAK
(Quercus spp.)

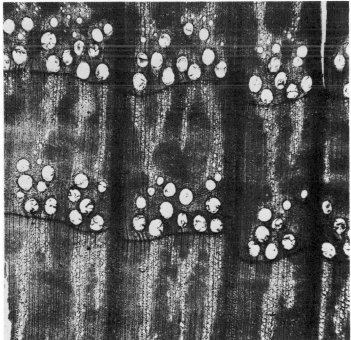

End-grain cross section (15x)

on gray twigs. The bark of most of the white oaks is light gray to an almost whitish gray, consisting of loose plates or ridges.

White oak is a very decay-resistant wood. It is quite heavy and hard, with a density of 45 lbs/ft³ or .76 g/cc at 12% M.C. The sapwood is light in color, while the heartwood is a rich yellow brown, turning to almost a tobacco color with age. The rays are larger than those of red oak. They are usually one inch (2.5 cm) or larger, sometimes up to 3 or 4 inches (7.5−10 cm). The pores are more angular, smaller, and thinner walled than those of red oak. Tyloses clog the pores, which makes the wood ideal for tight cooperage and shipbuilding. Its durability lends itself well for fence posts, railroad ties, and mine timbers. It is also used for millwork, furniture construction, kitchen cabinets, chairs, baskets, veneer, plywood, flooring, and agricultural implements. All oaks are slow and difficult to dry. They have a reputation for doing a good bit of their drying on the job.

Face grain

AMERICAN ELM
(Ulmus americana)

Ulmus is the classical Latin name for the elms. The American elm is sometimes called the white elm. Its range extends from Newfoundland to Saskatchewan, south to Texas, and east to Florida. Elms often grow 80–100 feet (24–30 m). They are among the most popular shade trees, with their arched, fanlike branches. Unfortunately, the elm is beginning to disappear in many areas, a victim of Dutch elm disease.

The alternate leaves are in the shape of a pointed, lopsided oval with a double-toothed margin. They are 2–5 inches (5–13 cm) long and 1–3 inches (2.5–7.5 cm) wide. Elm seeds ripen in early summer. They are flat and entirely surrounded by a papery wing, about ½ inch (1.2 cm) in diameter and notched at one end. Elm bark is a grayish brown and consists of long, interwoven ridges.

The wood is moderately hard and heavy, with a density of 35 lbs/ft³ or .56 g/cc at 12% M.C. Sapwood is a light tan, and the heartwood is a medium brown with an occasional reddish tinge. Rays are too small to be seen, and the pores grow in a ring-porous arrangement. The grain is frequently interlocked, which

2–15. Elm, *Ulmus americana,* grows 80–100 feet (24–30 m). (End-grain cross section, courtesy Ripon Microslides)

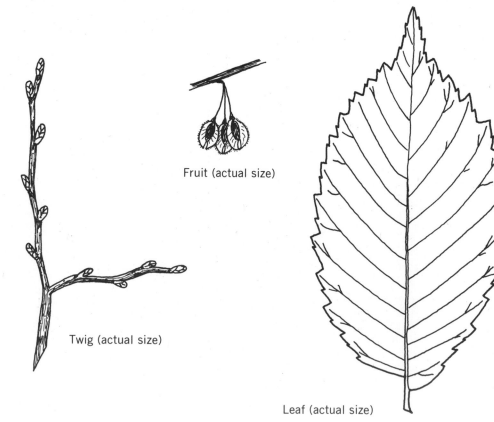

Twig (actual size)

Fruit (actual size)

Leaf (actual size)

Bark

AMERICAN ELM
(Ulmus americana)

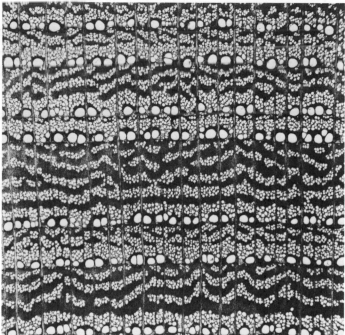

End-grain cross section (15x)

Face grain

makes splitting and chiseling very difficult. This even limits its use as firewood. Commercially it is used for slack cooperage, crates, boxes, pallets, veneer, and plywood. Its strength, toughness, and good bending qualities make it useful for furniture construction, upholstered frames, farm vehicles, interior trim, and novelties.

OSAGE ORANGE
(*Maclura pomifera*)

Maclura (Named for William McClure) *pomifera* (pome or apple bearing) also goes by the name Bois-d'Arc, or bowwood, since it is popularly used in the construction of archery bows. A member of the mulberry family, it was originally found in the area of the Arkansas and Red rivers, the home of the Osage Indians. Its hardiness and drought-resistant qualities have encouraged its planting as a windbreak and along fence lines throughout the southeastern United States. The tree is short and compact, with arched branches, and rarely grows taller than 50 feet (15 m).

Osage orange leaves are glossy and simple; they grow alternately on the thorny twigs. Clusters of small greenish flowers form large (3–5 inch or 7.5–12.5 cm), pale green, warty fruits similar to oranges. They exude a milky sap and are not edible. The bark is an orange brown and grows in long, shreddy ridges.

2–16. Osage orange, *Maclura pomifera*, grows to only 50 feet (15 m). (End-grain cross section, courtesy Ripon Microslides)

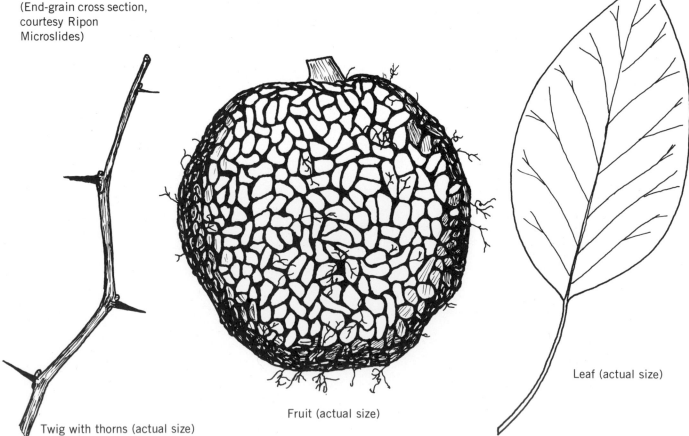

Twig with thorns (actual size)

Fruit (actual size)

Leaf (actual size)

Bark

OSAGE ORANGE
(Maclura pomifera)

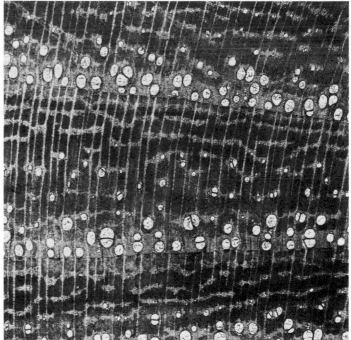

End-grain cross section (15x)

Osage orange sapwood is lemon yellow, and the heartwood is bright golden yellow, which turns a reddish brown with age. The yellow dye present in the wood is soluble in warm water. The wood is exceedingly heavy and hard, with a density of 56 lbs/ft³ or .84 g/cc at 12% M.C. The pores, which grow in a ring-porous manner, are completely filled with tyloses. Osage orange is very decay resistant, even in contact with soil, and is used for fences and posts. Its flexibility, strength, and straight grain make it the choice wood for archery bows. Commercially it is used for pulleys, treenails in shipbuilding, insulator pins on telephone poles, and machinery parts. When available in sufficient quantity, it makes a unique and sturdy cabinet wood.

Face grain

TULIP POPLAR
(*Liriodendron tulipifera*)

Tulip poplar is known locally as tuliptree, yellow poplar, or white wood. It is not a poplar (*Populus*) at all, but a member of the magnolia family. *Liriodendron* comes from the Greek words for lily tree, and *tulipifera* means tulip bearing. The tree is one of the largest timber producers in the east, with tree heights of 150 feet (45 m) and diameters of 3—4 feet (.9—1.2 m) the rule rather than the exception. In the forest the first limbs will appear at 60—70 feet (18—21 m) on the straight trunk. Tulip poplars are found from New England to Michigan, and from the Mississippi River east.

The leaf is wide, light green, and truncated in shape, and 4—6 inches (10—15 cm) across. The flowers resemble green and orange tulips, which turn into green and then brown fruit cones in the fall. These remain upright on the tree through most of the winter. Twigs are thick and stubby with alternate reddish buds. The deeply furrowed ash-gray bark can be 2—5 inches (5—13 cm) thick.

The sapwood is a creamy tan, while the heartwood is greenish tan with streaks of gray and pink. Tulip poplar has a disagreeable odor when green, which only gets worse with age, reaching rankness in antique furniture. The wood is light in weight, with a density of only

2—17. Tulip poplar, *Liriodendron tulipifera*, can grow to 150 feet (45 m). (End-grain cross section, courtesy Ripon Microslides)

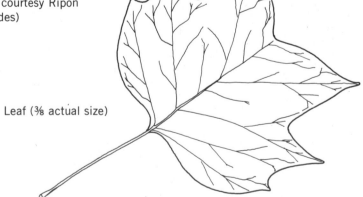

Leaf (⅜ actual size)

Twig (actual size)   Fruit (actual size)

Bark

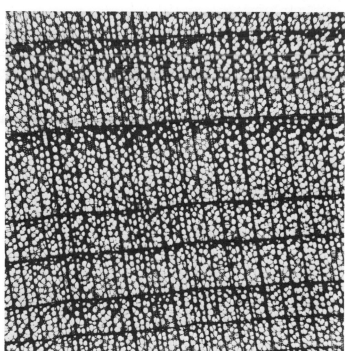
End-grain cross section (15x)

Face grain

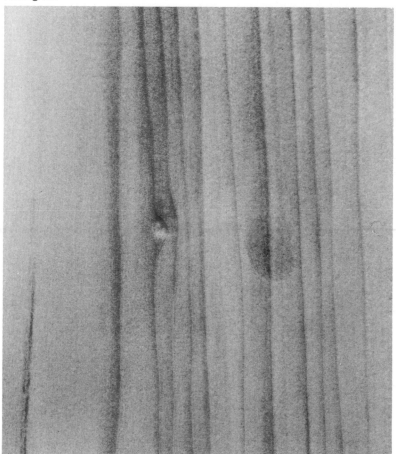

about 30 lbs/ft³ or .47 g/cc at 12% M.C. The vast amounts of clear wood have always been popular with cabinetmakers, especially as a secondary wood. Occasionally it is stained and passed off as walnut. It is a good carving wood and is used widely as a veneer and in lumber core plywood. Tulip poplar is also used in painted furniture, millwork, interior trim, boxes, crates, coffins, and even novelty items.

SASSAFRAS
(Sassafras albidum)

Sassafras is the Indian name given to the tree, while *albidum* is Latin, meaning white in color. It is a member of the laurel family and is sometimes called saxifrax. Its natural range is from Maine through southern Ontario, southwest to Illinois, Oklahoma, and Texas, and east to cental Florida. Seldom does sassafras become higher than 50 feet (15 m), although in the rich coves of the Great Smoky Mountains, the species reaches 90 feet (27 m). It is a slow-growing tree and can live 700−1000 years.

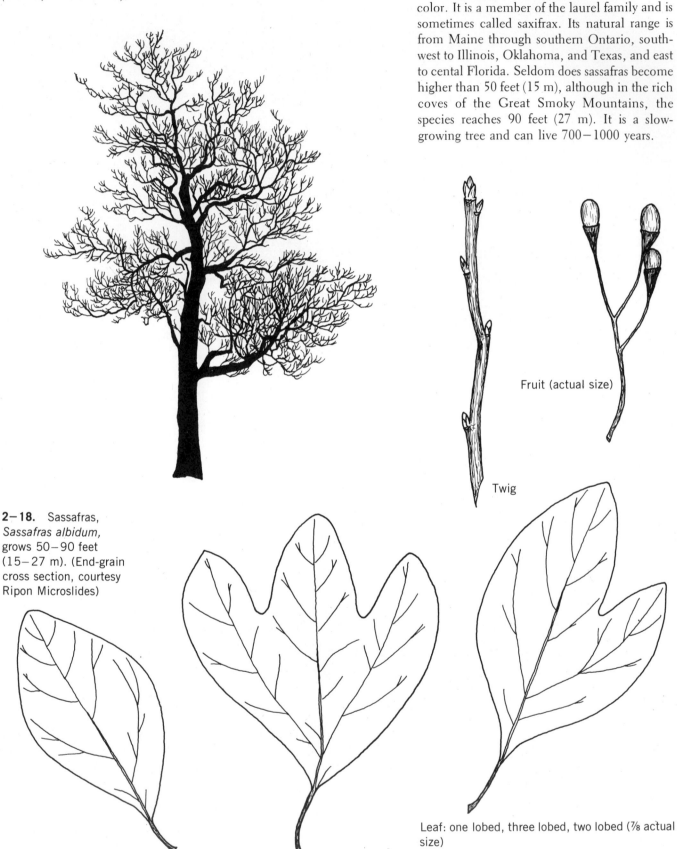

Fruit (actual size)

Twig

2−18. Sassafras, *Sassafras albidum,* grows 50−90 feet (15−27 m). (End-grain cross section, courtesy Ripon Microslides)

Leaf: one lobed, three lobed, two lobed (⅞ actual size)

Bark

SASSAFRAS
(Sassafras albidum)

End-grain cross section (15x)

The leaves grow in three different shapes on the same tree: lance, 3-pronged and mitten. In the fall they turn yellow, orange, and red. Fruits are small, dark-blue berrylike drupes, borne on a red, tapered stalk. The twigs and branches are extremely crooked and irregular. All parts of the tree contain aromatic oils: the leaves when crushed give off a spicy odor; twigs and bark are distilled for oil used in candy, medicine, and soap; the root bark is used for tea and root beer.

Sassafras sapwood consists of only 6–10 rings and is light yellow in color. The heartwood is faded yellow brown in color and very aromatic. With age it darkens and loses its spicy odor. The wood's texture is similar to ash or oak. It is ring porous, the pores filled with tyloses. Rays are barely visible. Straight grained and fairly soft, it has a density of only 32 lbs/ft³ or .52 g/c at 12% M.C. Decay resistance is high. It is used for house sills, fence posts, siding, and small-boat construction. Sassafras makes a good, easy-to-work cabinet wood. Its neutral color allows it to be used with other woods. As a secondary wood it imparts a spicy aroma to the contents of a cabinet.

Face grain

SWEET GUM
(*Liquidambar styraciflua*)

Sweet gum is not related to the other gums, the tupelos, but belongs to the witch hazel family. In some areas it is known as star-leaved gum, red gum, or bilstead. The Latin name *Liquidambar* refers to the sweet sap that exudes from the bark. This yellowish fluid is collected and marketed as storax, used in perfumes. *Styraciflua* is the older name for the genus, meaning styrax flower. Sweet gum grows best in moist river-bottom lands, fertile valleys, and coastal plains. It is found from Connecticut to Illinois, Missouri, and Texas, and east to central Florida. Often it reaches heights of 80—100 feet (24—30 m). In forests its trunk is usually clear for two-thirds of its height, while in the open it forms a broad, rounded, pyramidal crown.

Sweet gum leaves grow alternately and are star shaped with 5 (sometimes 7) points. They are aromatic when crushed and turn bright orange red to reddish purple in the fall. Twigs are reddish brown and develop corky ridges or wings after the second year. The bark is dark gray, warty, and furrowed. Male and female flowers form separately on the same tree. The pollen-producing flowers sit in bunches on small stems, while the seed-forming flowers hang on slender threads at the bases of the outer leaves. By early fall the brown seed balls develop. These consist of multipronged burrs made up of individual horn-tipped capsules.

In the trade the light-colored sapwood is marketed as sapgum, while the brown and red streaked heartwood is called red gum. Sweet

2—19. Sweet gum, *Liquidambar styraciflua*, grows 80—100 feet (24—30 m). (End-grain cross section, courtesy Ripon Microslides)

Twig (½ actual size)

Fruit (½ actual size)

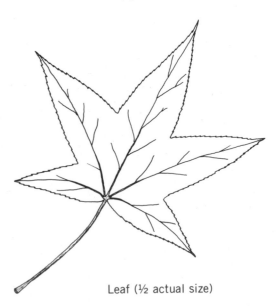

Leaf (½ actual size)

Bark

SWEET GUM
(Liquidambar styraciflua)

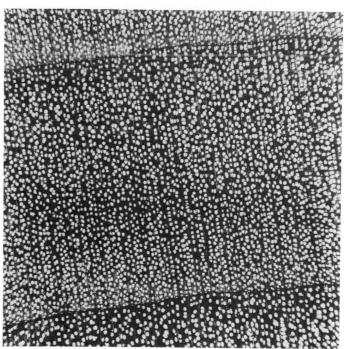

End-grain cross section (15x)

Face grain

gum is known for its pigment figure. The wood is diffuse porous, the pores being too small to be seen by eye. A wood of medium hardness, it has a density of 35 lbs/ft³ or .60 g/cc at 12% M.C. Red gum is widely used for veneer and is sometimes sold as satin walnut. Its color and figure make it a good cabinet wood. It is also used for boxes, flooring, and trim.

SYCAMORE
(Platanus occidentalis)

Platanus is the classical Latin name for the plane tree and *occidentalis* refers to its location in the western hemisphere. It is also known as button wood, plane tree, or water beech. Sycamore is a massive tree often reaching heights of 100−160 feet (30−49 m), and diameters of 2−5 feet (.6−1.5 m). The large, spreading branches form an irregular and open crown. Sycamores are found from Maine to Nebraska, south to central Texas, and east to northern Florida.

The leaves are simple and alternate, 3−5 lobed, from 4−10 inches (10−25 cm) long and equally wide. The bark consist of mottled patches of gray, brown, olive, and tan over a smooth surface of yellowish white. Inconspicuous flowers develop into a compact fruit-ball composed of dense, hairy, nutlike seeds. These remain on the tree, dangling from their slender stems until the following spring.

Sapwood is light tan to reddish brown, and heartwood is a deeper reddish brown. The wood is diffuse porous with numerous distinct rays. These form a noticeable fleck pattern on the radial surfaces and a series of closely spaced lines on tangential ones. The grain is interlocked, changing directions every few years. This results in a tough, hard-to-split wood which is used, on end, in professional butchers' blocks. The wood has a density of about 34 lbs/ft³ or .54 g/cc at 12% M.C. Sycamore is not very decay resistant and should not be used outdoors. Commercially it is used for baskets, cigar boxes, paneling, millwork, and as a sec-

2−20. Sycamore, *Platanus occidentalis*, grows 100−160 feet (30−49 m). (End-grain cross section, courtesy Ripon Microslides)

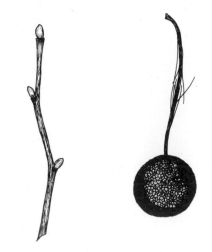

Twig (½ actual size)   Fruit (½ actual size)

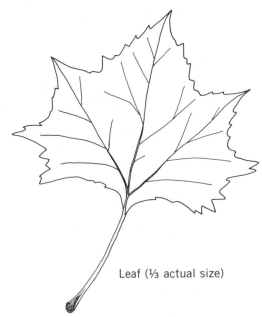

Leaf (⅓ actual size)

SYCAMORE
(Platanus occidentalis)

Bark

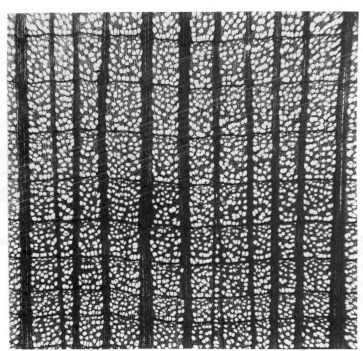

End-grain cross section (15x)

ondary wood. The unique, closely spaced, ray-patterned wood is underutilized as a primary wood in good furniture.

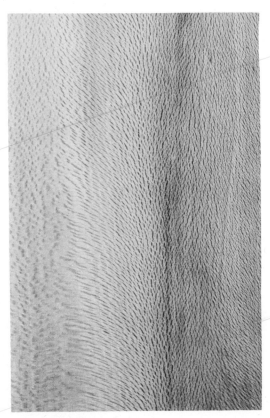

Face grain

APPLE
(*Malus pumila*)

Malus is the Latin name for apple, a[...] means dwarf or small. Even though [...] may be as American as apple pie, it is [...] migrant. Brought from Europe by the ear[...] tlers, the apple has established itself in al[...] all parts of the country and through most [...] southern Canada. Its wild cousin, the cra[...] apple, is a native, however. The apple is a member of the rose family. Under domestic conditions the apple is usually pruned to discourage a central trunk. A standard tree seldom reaches higher than 35 feet (10.5 m). Wild apples are found growing along fence rows, in old fields, and on abandoned farms. When the

2–21. Apple, *Malus pumila,* grows to only about 35 feet (10 m). (End-grain cross section, courtesy Ripon Microslides)

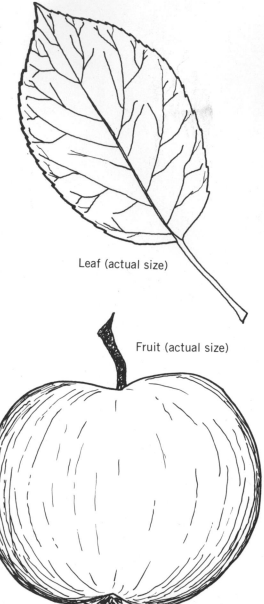

Leaf (actual size)

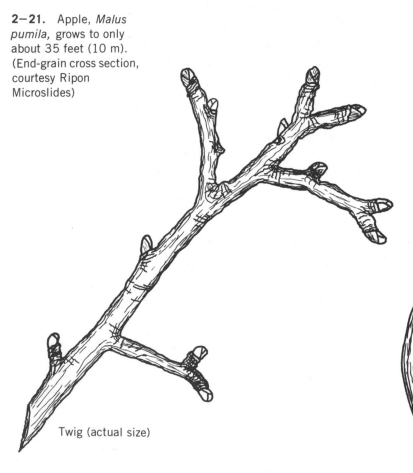

Twig (actual size)

Fruit (actual size)

APPLE
(Malus pumila)

Bark

End-grain cross section (15x)

forest reclaims the old fields, apple trees will sometimes grow to 60 feet (18 m) in an effort to compete for sunlight.

Apple leaves are simple pointed ovals with finely serrated edges. The fruits, familiar to almost everyone, range from the small, green, knobby, wild apple to the huge yellow-and-pink winter banana. Apple bark is grayish brown and scaly. Twigs are somewhat stubby, and wrinkled.

The apple is not known as a timber tree. It has, however, a solid wood of many uses. The sapwood is light tan, and the heartwood is a nutty brown. It is heavy and hard, with a density of 44 lbs/ft³ or .70 g/cc at 12% M.C. Sharp tools are necessary to work with apple. It is a wood almost made for lathe work. Taking a high polish, its fine grain structure allows it to be turned to intricate detail. It is used for furniture, turnings, toys, fruit presses, shuttles, wood screws, plane blocks, mallet heads, umbrella handles, and golf-club heads. Nothing smells sweeter than opening a drawer made of apple wood. Its pleasant aroma makes it a favorite for smoking meat, and it ranks high as a firewood. It is not decay resistant.

Face grain

BLACK CHERRY
(Prunus serotina)

Black cherry, sometimes called American, wild, or rum cherry, is a member of the rose family. *Prunus* is the Latin name for plum, and *serotina* means late, referring to the fact that black cherry blooms later than the other cherries. Cherry is found from Nova Scotia through southern Canada to Minnesota, south to Texas, and east to central Florida. It grows 60–100 feet (18–30 m) tall and 2–3 feet (.6–.9 m) in diameter.

The leaves, poisonous when eaten by livestock, are lance shaped with fine teeth along the

Fruit (actual size)

2–22. Black cherry, *Prunus serotina,* reaches 60–100 feet (18–30 m). (End-grain cross section, courtesy Ripon Microslides)

Leaf (actual size)

Twig (actual size)

Bark

BLACK CHERRY
(Prunus serotina)

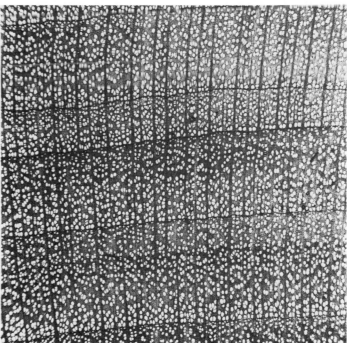

End-grain cross section (15x)

Face grain

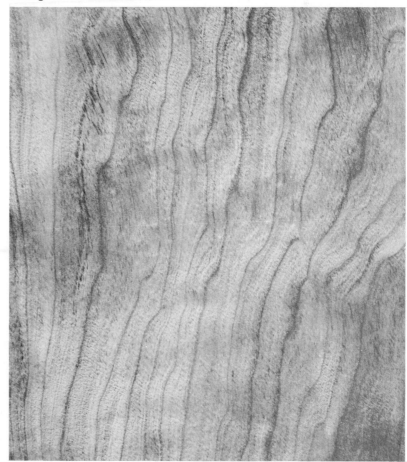

margins. They range 2−5 inches (5−12.5 cm) in length and grow alternately on thin, shiny, red-brown twigs. Cherry bark is dark and scaly, growing in irregular patches. The black, pea-sized fruits grow on small stems off a main stem. Used in wine making, they have a slightly bitter flavor and a large pit.

Cherry wood, once known as poor man's mahogany, has traditionally been one of the most popular of American cabinet woods. The cream-colored sapwood is only about 10−12 rings wide. Freshly cut, the heartwood is a pink-ish brown, aging to a beautiful deep reddish brown. Cherry achieves this natural patina fast-er than any other native wood. Mass-produced cherry furniture is usually heavily stained to hide the reddish hue. With a density of about 35 lbs/ft³ or .56 g/cc at 12% M.C., it is heavy and hard enough to wear well, yet soft enough to work comfortably with hand tools. The pores are small, and the wood is diffuse porous. Rays are also small, but visible. Properly seasoned, cherry is quite stable and warps very little. Con-sequently, it is used for all sorts of cabinet and chair work, veneer, scientific instruments, piano actions, and printers' blocks for mounting electrotypes and etchings.

BLACK LOCUST
(*Robinia pseudoacacia*)

2–23. Black locust, *Robinia pseudoacacia,* grows to 80 feet (24 m). (End-grain cross section, courtesy Ripon Microslides)

Robinia (named for the French herbalist Jean Robin) *pseudoacacia* (false acacia) is also known as yellow locust. It is a member of the legume family and has the ability to fix nitrogen from the air into the soil. Considered a weed tree by many because of its habit of sprouting suckers from its roots, this characteristic makes it valuable in soil erosion projects. Originally, locust was found only in the Ozark and Appalachian mountains but has been transplanted to almost all parts of the country. The tree grows to about 80 feet (24 m) with a diameter of 2–4 feet (.6–1.2 m) and lives only about 100 years.

The alternate, pinnately compound leaves have 7–19 rounded leaflets ranging 8–14 inches (20–35 cm) in length. Twigs zigzag away from the buds, giving the entire branch structure a gnarled, scraggly appearance. A pair of large thorns grows at the nodes, although a thornless variety (same species) also occurs. Locust blossoms are clusters of white, pealike flowers, which form thin, bean-shaped pods with 4–8 seeds. The bark is reddish brown to black with long, deep, interfacing furrows.

Black locust sapwood is yellowish and only 2–3 rings wide. The heartwood is yellow to greenish brown and ages to a beautiful reddish brown. It is extremely hard and heavy, with a

Leaves (½ actual size)

Bark

BLACK LOCUST
(Robinia pseudoacacia)

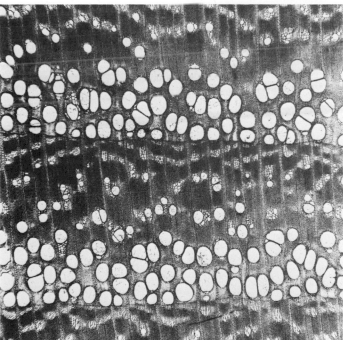

End-grain cross section (15x)

density of 48 lbs/ft³ or .77 g/cc at 12% M.C. The wood is ring porous with large pores filled with tyloses. Rays are distinct. Black locust ranks as one of the most decay-resistant species when in contact with soil. In the Appalachian Mountains it is said that locust "lasts two years longer than stone." Therefore, it is used for fence posts, foundations and mining timbers, railroad ties, insulator pins, telephone poles, and for treenails in boat building. In the shop it can be used for almost any cabinet work, although it dulls tools quickly.

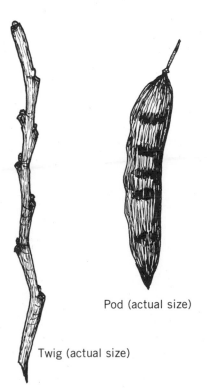

Pod (actual size)

Twig (actual size)

Face grain

HOLLY
(*Ilex opaca*)

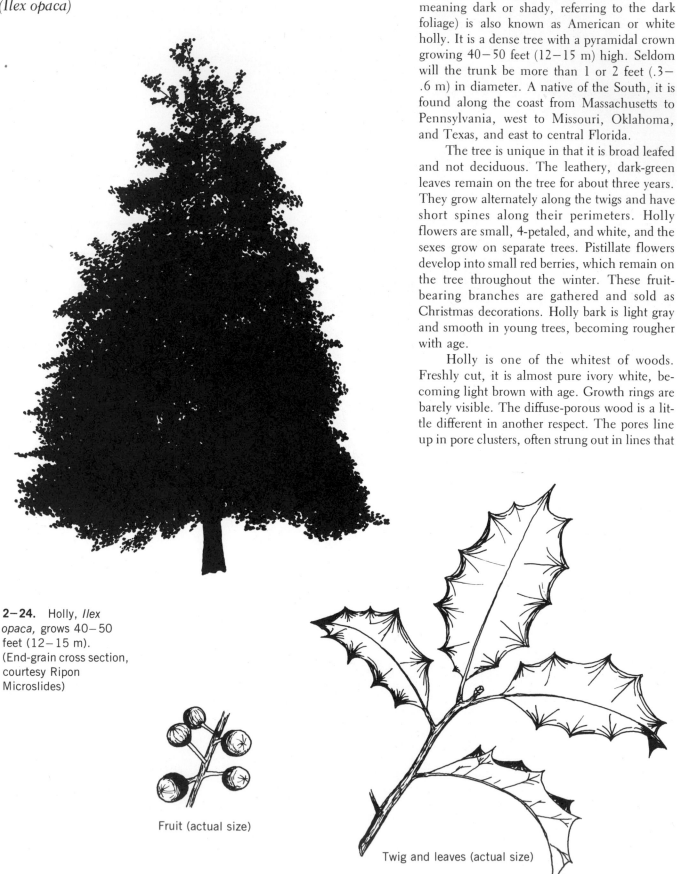

Ilex (Latin name of the holly oak) *opaca* (Latin, meaning dark or shady, referring to the dark foliage) is also known as American or white holly. It is a dense tree with a pyramidal crown growing 40—50 feet (12—15 m) high. Seldom will the trunk be more than 1 or 2 feet (.3—.6 m) in diameter. A native of the South, it is found along the coast from Massachusetts to Pennsylvania, west to Missouri, Oklahoma, and Texas, and east to central Florida.

The tree is unique in that it is broad leafed and not deciduous. The leathery, dark-green leaves remain on the tree for about three years. They grow alternately along the twigs and have short spines along their perimeters. Holly flowers are small, 4-petaled, and white, and the sexes grow on separate trees. Pistillate flowers develop into small red berries, which remain on the tree throughout the winter. These fruit-bearing branches are gathered and sold as Christmas decorations. Holly bark is light gray and smooth in young trees, becoming rougher with age.

Holly is one of the whitest of woods. Freshly cut, it is almost pure ivory white, becoming light brown with age. Growth rings are barely visible. The diffuse-porous wood is a little different in another respect. The pores line up in pore clusters, often strung out in lines that

2—24. Holly, *Ilex opaca,* grows 40—50 feet (12—15 m). (End-grain cross section, courtesy Ripon Microslides)

Fruit (actual size)

Twig and leaves (actual size)

Bark

HOLLY
(Ilex opaca)

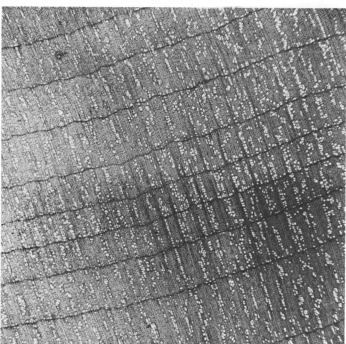

End-grain cross section (15x)

frequently cross ring boundaries. Holly is relatively hard and heavy, with a density of about 40 lbs/ft^3 or .63 g/cc at 12% M.C. It is used most often in veneer and inlay work, especially where a light-colored wood is desired. Other uses are as backs for engravings, and in scientific and musical instruments. In the cabinet shop holly is used for contrasting beads and moldings and for lathe turnings because of its fine grain and ability to take a polish. It is also suitable for carving, despite its hardness.

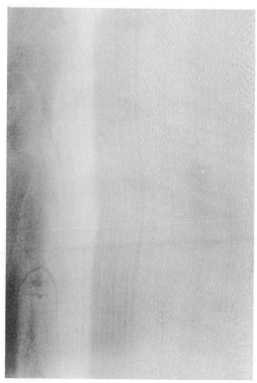

Face grain

SUGAR MAPLE
(*Acer saccharum*)

Acer (Latin for maple, from the Celtic meaning hard) *saccharum* (sweet or sugary, referring to the sap; not to be confused with A. *saccharinum*, the silver maple) is also called hard or rock maple or sugar tree. It is a tree of many uses, probably most noted for its syrup. Maple sap begins flowing in early spring and should be tapped during times of warm days and freezing nights. About forty gallons (152 liters) of sap yields one gallon (3.86 liters) of syrup. The maple is also prized as an ornamental, with its symmetrical oval crown. It reaches heights of 80−100 feet (24−30 m) and diameters of 2−4 feet (.6−1.2 m). The species prefers fertile soil but succeeds even in poor, rocky soil. Maple grows from Newfoundland through southern Canada to Minnesota, south to Louisiana, and east to Virginia.

The leaves, which turn a brilliant orange in the fall, are 5 lobed and smooth edged. They grow opposite one another on light-brown twigs. The fruits are double winged and grow in bunches. Sugar maple bark is ash gray and flaky, sometimes resembling the bark of the shagbark hickory.

Sugar maple sapwood is creamy white with a thickness of about 30−40 rings. The heartwood is light gray to reddish brown. Wavy, curly, or bird's eye figure is common. The rays, although small, are still visible by eye. The

2−25. Sugar maple, *Acer saccharum*, reaches 80−100 feet (24−30 m). (End-grain cross section, courtesy Ripon Microslides)

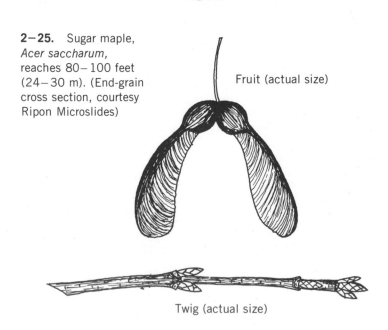

Fruit (actual size)

Twig (actual size)

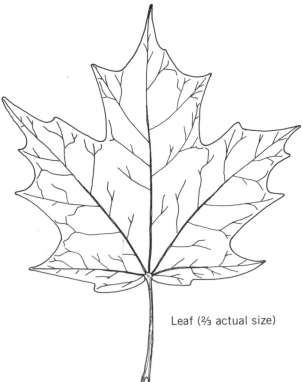

Leaf (⅔ actual size)

Bark

SUGAR MAPLE
(*Acer saccharum*)

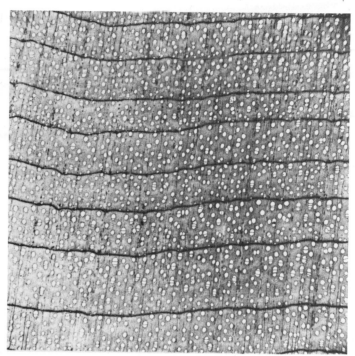

End-grain cross section (15x)

wood is diffuse porous, hard, and heavy, with a density of 44 lbs/ft³ or .70 g/cc at 12% M.C. It is used where a hard, long-wearing material is desired: flooring, bowling pins, shoe lasts, shuttles, bobbins, croquet mallets and balls, tool handles, and butchers' blocks. It is also very popular in cabinet work for all types of furniture as well as veneer, and for scientific instruments, piano pin blocks and frames, as well as other musical instruments.

Face grain

BASSWOOD
(*Tilia americana*)

Basswood is also known as whitewood, lime, or beetree, or more commonly American linden, which is the literal translation of its Latin name. It is a tall (60–100 feet, 18–30 m) stately tree, frequently used as an ornamental, and well adapted to city conditions. The species grows best in moist, fertile soil, where it grows rapidly but reaches only 100–140 years of age. Usually it grows with other hardwoods, very rarely in pure stands. Its natural range is from New Brunswick through southern Canada into Manitoba and North Dakota, south to Kansas and Arkansas, and east to North Carolina and Virginia.

Basswood leaves are asymmetrically heart shaped, about 4 inches (10 cm) long and 3 inches (7.5 cm) wide. The tree is highly prized by beekeepers for its fragrant, creamy white flowers. These hang in clusters attached by a single stalk to a leafy bract. Fruits form as small woody spheres. The bark is dark gray and in older trees is furrowed with flat, scaly ridges.

Basswood is very light in color, with white sapwood and creamy white to pale brown

2–26. Basswood, *Tilia americana,* grows from 60–100 feet (18–30 m). (End-grain cross section, courtesy Ripon Microslides)

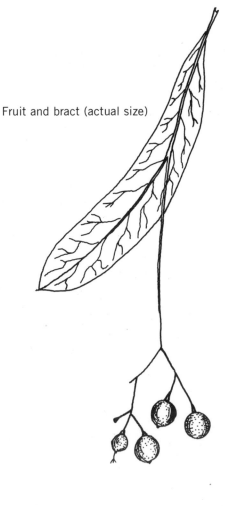

Fruit and bract (actual size)

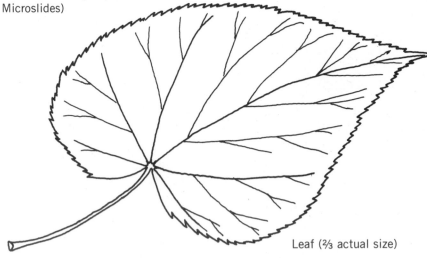

Leaf (⅔ actual size)

Bark

BASSWOOD
(Tilia americana)

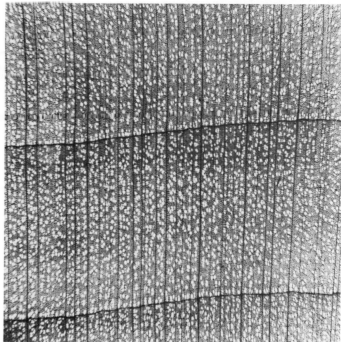

End-grain cross section (15x)

heartwood. In weight it is also light, having a density of only about 26 lbs/ft³ or .41 g/cc at 12% M.C. This relative softness makes it easy to indent with the thumbnail. It has a very faint odor when freshly cut, no taste, straight grain, and virtually no figure. The pores are diffuse and the growth rings are indistinct, with almost no difference in the hardness of early and late wood. The softness, even texture, and straight grain make it a favorite wood for carvers. These characteristics also make it a sought-after wood for tubs, excelsior, slack cooperage, boxes, apiary supplies, venetian blind slats, piano keys, and assorted wooden ware. Basswood warps and checks very little after drying and is frequently used as a secondary wood in furniture as well as for plywood and veneer.

Face grain

Twig (actual size)

FLOWERING DOGWOOD
(*Cornus florida*)

The Latin wood *Cornus* means horn and refers to the extremely hard wood; *florida* means flowering. Dogwood is a very small tree, rarely exceeding 40 feet (12 m) in height and 10–12 inches (25–30.5 cm) in diameter. It is a handsome, slow-growing ornamental with a wide crown and almost horizontal branches. Although it is planted in many parts of the country, its natural range is from southern New England to Michigan, south to Texas, and east to central Florida.

Dogwood is commonly thought of as an ornamental, with a wide irregular crown and white 4-petaled flowers that appear in the spring, prior to the leaves. These petals are actually the bractlike bud covers, while the true flower is the small yellow portion in the center. Fruits consist of small clusters of scarlet berries, each containing a large seed. The leaves are opposite, elliptical, and pointed, 3–6 inches (7.5–15 cm) long. They have a heavy midrib and 4–7 veins, curving toward the margins.

2–27. Dogwood, *Cornus florida*, grows to only about 40 feet (12 m). (End-grain cross section, courtesy Ripon Microslides)

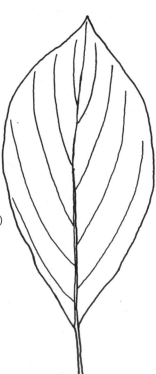

Fruit (actual size)

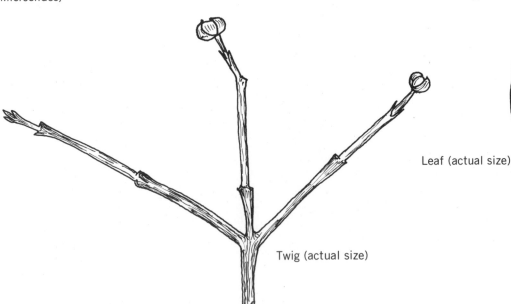

Twig (actual size)

Leaf (actual size)

FLOWERING DOGWOOD
(Cornus florida)

Bark

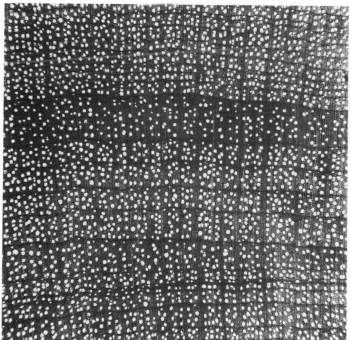

End-grain cross section (15x)

Face grain

Dogwood bark is reddish brown to almost black, consisting of small individual plates.

The sapwood consists of 30—40 rings and is a creamy tan to purplish or pinkish brown. The heartwood, present in older trees, is dark brown, often variegated. Dogwood has a spicy odor when sawn. It is an extremely heavy and hard wood, with a density of 51 lbs/ft^3 or .81 g/cc at 12% M.C. The pores of this diffuse-porous wood are too small to be seen by eye. Rays are visible and plentiful. Dogwood takes a tremendous shine and, when worked on the lathe, can be turned to intricate detail and polished to appear the texture of ivory. It is used in industry to produce weaving shuttles and bobbins, golf-club heads, and machinery bearings. Other uses include hinge pins, mallet heads, knobs, and other items subject to high wear and friction. It is usually not available in quantities sufficient for large cabinets.

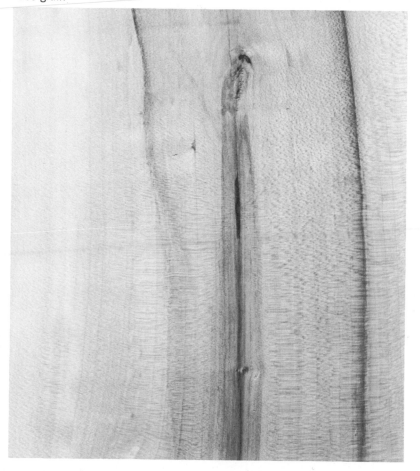

PERSIMMON
(Diospyros virginiana)

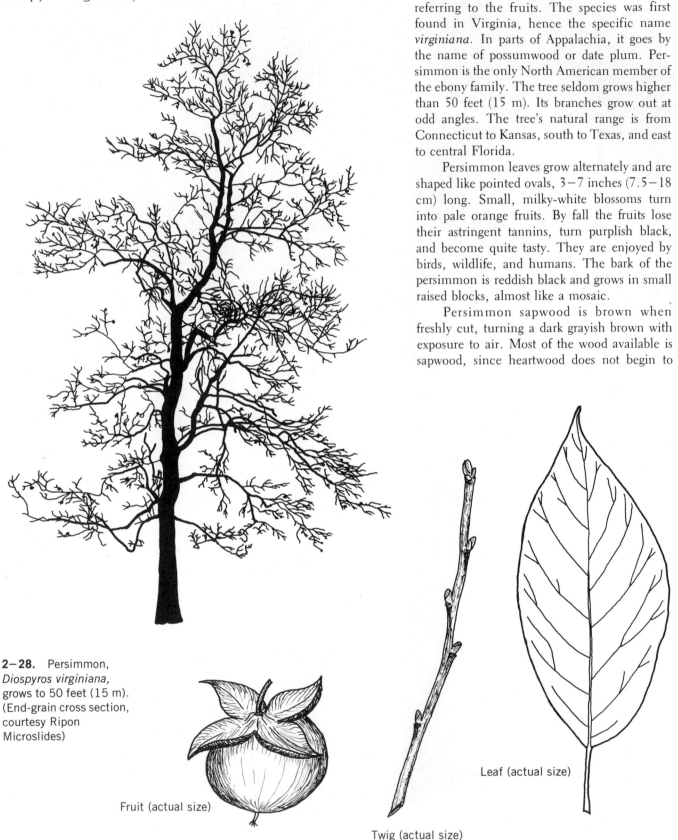

Diospyros comes from the Greek *dios* (god) and *purous* (grain), meaning food for the gods, referring to the fruits. The species was first found in Virginia, hence the specific name *virginiana*. In parts of Appalachia, it goes by the name of possumwood or date plum. Persimmon is the only North American member of the ebony family. The tree seldom grows higher than 50 feet (15 m). Its branches grow out at odd angles. The tree's natural range is from Connecticut to Kansas, south to Texas, and east to central Florida.

Persimmon leaves grow alternately and are shaped like pointed ovals, 3–7 inches (7.5–18 cm) long. Small, milky-white blossoms turn into pale orange fruits. By fall the fruits lose their astringent tannins, turn purplish black, and become quite tasty. They are enjoyed by birds, wildlife, and humans. The bark of the persimmon is reddish black and grows in small raised blocks, almost like a mosaic.

Persimmon sapwood is brown when freshly cut, turning a dark grayish brown with exposure to air. Most of the wood available is sapwood, since heartwood does not begin to

2–28. Persimmon, *Diospyros virginiana*, grows to 50 feet (15 m). (End-grain cross section, courtesy Ripon Microslides)

Fruit (actual size)

Twig (actual size)

Leaf (actual size)

Bark

PERSIMMON
(Diospyros virginiana)

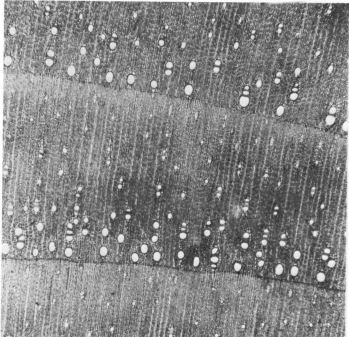

End-grain cross section (15x)

form for at least 100 years. When present, it is blackish brown to black. The semi—ring-porous wood has earlywood pores large enough to be seen by eye. Individual rays are indistinct but can be seen as tiny ripple marks on the tangential surface. Persimmon is very heavy and hard, with a density of 52 lbs/ft³ or .78 g/cc at 12% M.C. This quality makes it commercially valuable in the manufacture of spools, shuttles, golf-club heads, and shoe lasts (now being replaced by the cheaper, softer, and more plentiful rock maple). In cabinet work it is used in areas of wear and friction or where a darker wood is desired.

Face grain

WHITE ASH
(*Fraxinus americana*)

White ash (American ash in Latin) also goes by the names of Biltmore ash and cane ash. The ashes are members of the olive family, and white ash is commercially the most important of the genus. The trees are up to 80 feet tall (24 m) with a broadly oval crown and opposite branches. White ash grows from Nova Scotia west to Minnesota, south to Texas, and east to Florida.

Ash trees are quite similar to each other, and a good tree manual is needed to separate the species. White ash leaves are pinnately compound, with 5−7 leaflets. The foliage turns yellowish to purplish brown in the fall. Fruits are winged, long and thin, and grow in bunches, while the twigs are thick and stubby. It is not inconceivable that ash got its name because the color of its ridged bark recalls the color of wood ashes. Younger trees are smooth barked, although the same ash-gray color.

In figure and texture, white ash is similar to oak in its open grain. Smaller pored than oak, ash is a ring-porous wood, and its rays are barely visible by eye. The cream-colored sapwood contrasts with the light-brown to gray-brown heartwood. Ash has a characteristic odor when sawn, which becomes more pronounced when the blade is dull and begins to burn the wood. Of all the ash species, white ash is the

2−29. White ash, *Fraxinus americana*, reaches 80 feet in height (24 m). (End-grain cross section, courtesy Ripon Microslides)

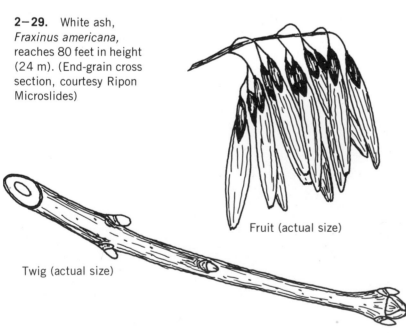

Fruit (actual size)

Twig (actual size)

Leaves (⅓ actual size)

Bark

WHITE ASH
(Fraxinus americana)

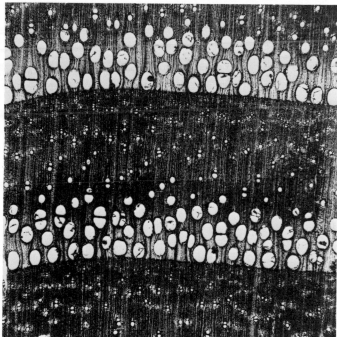

End-grain cross section (15x)

most lustrous. Operations such as planing, chiseling, and boring are relatively easy. It will splinter and tear, however, if dull tools are used. It is hard and heavy, with a density of 42 lbs/ft³ or .67 g/cc at 12% M.C. Strength, shock resistance, straight grain, and the ability to bend make white ash a wood much in demand by industry and craftsmen alike. Its shock resistance makes it the choice wood in the manufacture of baseball bats. Long tool handles as in rakes and shovels, axes and hammers, are produced from white ash because of its straight grain and elasticity. This last property also makes it an ideal material for hockey sticks, paddles, and oars. Its ability to bend, green or steamed, makes it useful for snowshoe, tennis racket, and bentwood furniture production. It is also used in veneers, baskets, cabinets, truck bodies and wagons, and novelty items. In a pinch it burns reasonably well, unseasoned, as firewood.

Face grain

HARDY CATALPA
(*Catalpa speciosa*)

The name *Catalpa* comes not from the Latin, but from the Cherokee Indian name for the tree, while *speciosa* is Latin for showy or ornamental, referring to the flowers. The hardy catalpa is also known as the cigar tree, catawba tree, and northern or western catalpa, to distinguish it from the southern or common catalpa (*C. bignonioides*). The tree reaches heights of up to 100 feet (30 m) and diameters of 2–4 feet (.6–1.2 m). Its natural range includes the states of Arkansas, Missouri, Illinois, Indiana, Kentucky, and Tennessee, although it has spread and is planted as an ornamental as far away as New England.

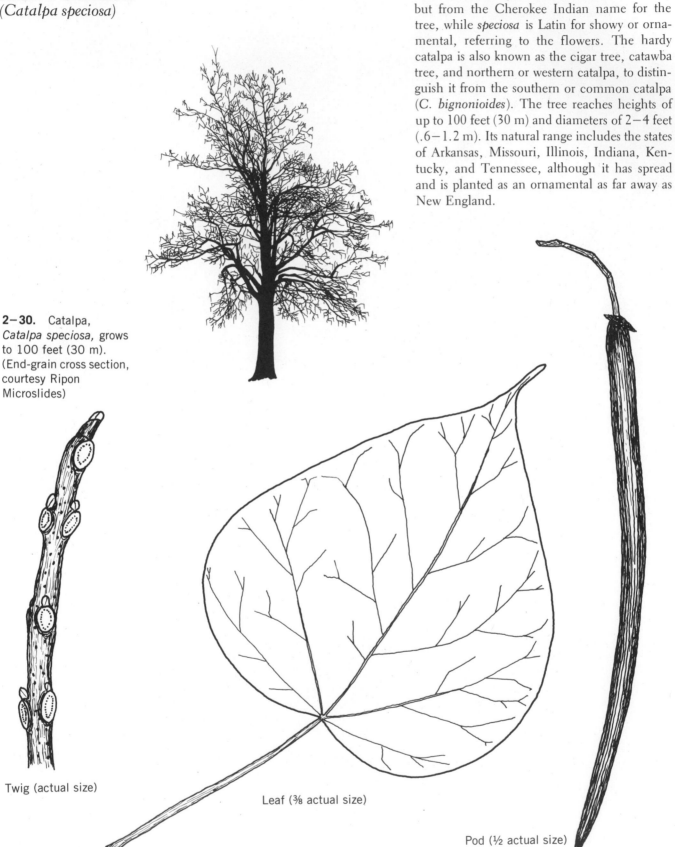

2–30. Catalpa, *Catalpa speciosa,* grows to 100 feet (30 m). (End-grain cross section, courtesy Ripon Microslides)

Twig (actual size)

Leaf (⅜ actual size)

Pod (½ actual size)

HARDY CATALPA
(Catalpa speciosa)

Bark

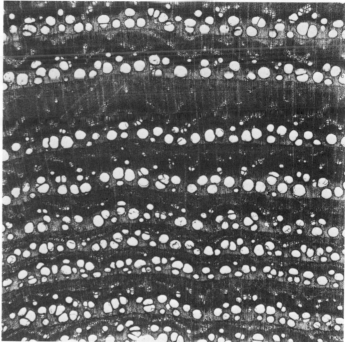

End-grain cross section (15x)

Face grain

Catalpa leaves are about 10 inches (25 cm) long and 7 inches (17.5 cm) wide and heart shaped; they grow in whorls of three. In the spring large white flowers grow in erect clusters at the ends of the twigs. By fall these turn into slender beanlike fruits 10—20 inches (25—50 cm) long. Catalpa bark is a light grayish brown and consists of flat, scaly ridges.

Catalpa has pale, extremely narrow sapwood for only one or two rings. The heartwood is grayish brown, straight grained, and similar in appearance to butternut. The large pores grow in a ring-porous manner. Rays are almost invisible. The wood is soft and light in weight, with a density of only about 29 lbs/ft³ or .46 g/cc at 12% M.C. Catalpa is decay resistant, even when in contact with soil. Thus, it is used for fence posts and railroad ties. Occasionally it is used for interior work. It lends itself well to carving, although as a cabinet wood it is difficult to sand and its softness makes it prone to denting. Most commercially cut catalpa goes into veneer production.

CHAPTER 3

WOODLOT MANAGEMENT AND HARVEST

INVENTORY OF EXISTING GROWTH

Obviously, it is not possible for every woodworker to own a private woodlot. Yet a basic knowledge of the management, harvest, and sawing process is essential in order to gain a full understanding of the material. Anyone working in wood should have the opportunity to cut a tree at least once in his or her life. That experience alone imparts a totally new respect for wood. Standing before the tree and looking up at its huge mass, one cannot help being awed by this living thing that has endured for so many years. It is a humbling feeling that instills an obligation to use the material wisely.

Those fortunate enough to have access to a woodlot or even a few dozen trees can share in the pride of producing furniture with wood grown on their own land. A few hours spent working in the woods each month pays dividends not only in increased and better-quality lumber and firewood, but also in fresh air, exercise, and a fuller understanding of the forest ecosystem, as well as a more valuable piece of land.

But before any management plan is drawn up, the owner should be familiar with the land, and an inventory of existing growth must be made. The best way to accomplish this is by walking the land. Begin by observing the dominant growth, that is, the most abundant species. A field guide to trees and a small notebook are helpful. Becoming thoroughly familiar with one or two species at a time is probably the easiest approach. It is also helpful to identify trees at all times of the year, not only during the warm months when they are in full foliage. With some practice, time, and a guidebook, trees can be recognized by their basic shape, branch structure, buds, leaf scars, and bark. This is especially helpful since the ideal time for cutting is during the dormant, leafless months.

Record the various species on a rough map of the property. Usually, specific locations will favor certain species. North slopes will have different growth from south slopes; ridges will have different growth from wetter, more fertile areas.

Aerial photos, available free from the Soil Conservation Service (part of the U.S.D.A.), are extremely useful in grouping timber stands (figure 3–1). Once the various groups have been located and identified, they can be recorded on the map with the help of the aerial photo. Property lines should be established and verified.

Details can now be filled in. Include unusually large trees, old hollow trees, rare trees, overgrown areas needing thinning, and storm-damaged and diseased trees. Don't forget basic topographic features, old logging roads, creeks, open fields, stone walls, and rock outcroppings. Knowledge of the locations of these features will aid in the formation of the management plan. The map itself will now suggest areas that

CONSERVATION PLAN MAP

Owner_____ Operator_____

County_____ State_____ Date_____

Approximate acres_____ _____ Approximate scale 1"= 660'

—N Cooperating with_____Conservation District

PLAN IDENTIFICATION_____ PHOTO NUMBER 1975 PHOTO_____

ASSISTED BY_____ USDA SOIL CONSERVATION SERVICE

3-1. Aerial photograph of mixed forest land. (courtesy U.S.D.A. Soil Conservation Service)

clearly need immediate attention and will aid in forming the objectives of the management plan.

OBJECTIVES OF THE MANAGEMENT PLAN

With the existing growth mapped and accounted for, the next step is to outline the objectives of the plan. A list of the following will be helpful:

1. Amount of wood immediately available. This includes trees that are diseased or deformed and those past maturity. Signs of age are heartwood rot (hollow), large numbers of broken branches, split trunks, dead branches, and disease and insect infestation (figure 3-2).

2. Estimate of the average annual harvest. After the first cutting of sick and overmature trees, the harvest thereafter should be on a sustained yield basis. This means the cutting must be balanced with the generation of new growth.

3–2. Overmature, overgrown white pine.

Naturally, this is a matter of judgment over the course of several seasons. If the stand is of mixed-age trees, it will be apparent after a few years if the harvest is too high or too low. If too low, the full potential of new growth will not be utilized; if too high, new growth will not keep pace with the harvest.

3. Species to be encouraged. Depending on the native species of the area, the determination of which wood is most desirable is a personal decision.

4. Estimate of the average annual firewood production. Firewood is a very important income-producing product of the woodlot. Firewood production far outweighs that of nice, clear butt logs of furniture quality. Trees that are crooked, diseased, frost-, fire-, or storm-damaged are candidates for the stove. Trees needing to be thinned out are also relegated to the fuel pile. One-third to two-thirds of the volume of a timber tree is in branches, knots, crotches, and stumps, all of which can go as firewood. Branches usually consist of reaction wood and are therefore useless from a cabinetmaker's viewpoint. A line must be drawn between firewood and lumber, however. Many an ignorant landowner cuts the straightest trees for firewood because they split better! A cord (4'x4'x8' or 1.22x1.22x2.44 m) contains 128 cubic feet (3.58 m³) of wood and air. Assuming a "tight" cord actually contains 85 cubic feet (2.4 m³) of solid wood, that equals about 500 board feet sawn! At a low price of $.60/board foot for hardwood, that amounts to $300 for lumber, compared to one-fifth to one-tenth that price for firewood. Good judgment pays off.

5. Areas set aside for wildlife or recreational use. These can include steep, rocky areas and wet sections. Space permitting, an occasional hollow den tree can be left for squirrels and raccoons. A well-managed woodlot need not exclude wildlife; the two are compatible. In the north, for instance, during severe winters, deer will come from miles around searching for food at the sound of a chain saw. After forage within their reach has been exhausted, tender buds from treetops are very welcome.

The woodlot can also be used for other types of recreation—photography, hiking, camping, cross-country skiing.

6. Areas needing immediate attention. These are the aforementioned trees—the sick, damaged, and old, as well as heavy stands in need of thinning.

7. Replanting. If there is any open or unused land, consider replanting. It is both a joy and a frustration: a joy in that suddenly there is a whole acre of young pine, walnut, or maple; a frustration in that it will be 40–100 years until harvest. The trees will add value to the land and will earn the landowner the respect of his descendants. The local state forester should be consulted before investing in nursery stock. He will recommend native plants compatible with the soil type. Where natural reseeding does not take place, it is a good idea to replant areas that have already been cut.

Taking these points into account will give the landowner a fairly clear idea of what is available, what can be expected, and what needs to be done. If properly managed, a small woodlot can yield ample lumber, firewood from the culls, prunings, and thinnings, and still allow for wildlife and recreation. This concept is known as *multiple use.*

MANAGEMENT BASICS

One of the landowner's objectives is to manage the woodlot in such a manner as to produce a higher quality of timber in a shorter period of time. By practicing timber stand improvement, the landowner is merely speeding up and redirecting an otherwise natural process.

The amount of growth that can take place per acre per year is limited by the fertility of the soil, annual precipitation, and exposure to light. Therefore, under specific conditions, only a limited amount of growth can take place annually. This is the *carrying capacity* of the land. Proper management can improve this carrying capacity, however, and affect the various forms any ensuing growth will take. For instance, an acre can support hundreds of thousands of seedlings (trees up to 3 feet high or .9 m), about 2,000 saplings (trees up to 4 inches or 10 cm in diameter), about 500 poles (trees 4—12 inches or 10—30 cm in diameter), or about 250 standards (trees 1—2 feet or 30—60 cm in diameter). Or that same acre could support a proportionate combination of any of those trees. It could be an even-aged stand where all the trees are roughly the same age, as occurs after a fire or a reforestation program. Or it could be a mixed-age stand, with all sizes from seedlings to standards present. That acre could support either a pure forest, with all of the same species, or a mixed forest, with several species.

Small trees obviously require less nutrients than large trees. Thus, as the seedlings grow into saplings, competition sets in among the trees, since there is only so much space, light, moisture, and food to go around. From the woodlot manager's point of view, competition within limits is desirable. Too little competition, for instance 8 or 10 seedlings per acre, will cause the trees to grow into their natural or field-grown shape, mostly branches and very little trunk. On the other hand, 2,000 saplings per acre, not thinned, will become thin and spindly, and the growth rate will drop. The amount of competition is dependent on the density of the stand. A rough idea of the stand density can be determined by simply looking at the forest canopy, or overhead branch cover. A medium-stocked stand, which promotes the best competition, has 40—70 percent of its canopy closed over (figure 3—3). An understocked stand has less than 40 percent of its canopy closed, while an overstocked stand has more than 70 percent. The right amount of competition promotes the growth of straight, tall trunks with few lateral branches. The effects of competition can even be seen in open-grown trees that were grown too close together (figure 3—4).

3—3 *(above).* A medium-stocked stand of white pine with 40—70 percent canopy cover.

3—4 *(left).* Open-grown, competing trees, with diminished branch growth between them.

THINNING

Thinning is necessary to assure proper growth for the remaining trees. While providing for growth, water and nutrient uptake and for sunlight absorption, it should yet allow enough competition for straight upward growth, with a minimum of lateral growth. Although thinning occurs naturally in the forest, this is a much slower, more inefficient process. For example, a one-acre field on the edge of the forest could be seeded by the surrounding trees and produce several thousand seedlings. They would grow

3—5 *(left).* Woodlot in need of thinning.

3—6 *(right).* Woodlot after thinning operation.

3—7. Pine seedling released from competition four years ago.

vigorously until they reached a certain size, at which time they would start to compete with each other. Over the next several years, the saplings would crowd each other and compete for available light, space, and nutrients to such a degree as to slow the growth rate of all trees on that acre. Eventually, those trees with the best location and the greatest size would crowd out and kill the weaker ones in order to assure their own survival. This process would continue over the next several decades, until only 200 to 500 mature trees remained on that one acre.

Artificial thinning of the woodlot would release the trees from too much competition, hence relieving the stress and allowing optimum growth to continue in the remaining trees at all times (figures 3-5 and 3-6). Ideally, thinning should take place before competition actually begins to slow the growth of the remaining trees. Figure 3—7 shows a pine sapling that clearly demonstrates the effects of this release from competition. White pines ordinarily grow whorls of five branches per year, the distance between the whorls indicating the amount of yearly growth. For the first several years the growth averaged 2—3 inches (5—7.5 cm). After the woodlot was thinned, the growth increased to 10—12 inches (25—30 cm) per year.

Actually deciding which trees to thin and which to leave is based on two factors: the worth or potential of the tree and the distance from other trees. Obviously the crooked, small, and diseased trees should pose no problems. The difficulty comes when there are several tall, straight, healthy trees growing close together. The size of the trees should act as a guide. Trees in the sapling to small pole stage can grow 6—8 feet (1.8—2.4 m) apart. Trees in the larger pole stage to smaller standard stage are better off with 10—15 foot (3—4.5 m) spacing, whereas trees in the larger standard stage can be spaced up to 20 feet (6 m) apart. Consequently, compromises must often be reached in which a good straight tree is cut because it is too close to other trees, while a marginal tree is left standing since its cutting would leave too big a void.

Often, trees will sprout from the stumps of those previously cut. This is especially true of deciduous trees. Sprouts from the stumps of young trees will be more vigorous and numerous than those from old trees. Stump sprouts have a tendency to grow away from each other or lean outward from the stump to minimize competition for light (figure 3−8). They usually get a head start on single seedlings and saplings because of the large root system. After several years the growth tends to slow, because the single root system cannot support five, six, or eight trees, no matter what its size. These sprouts should be thinned to the single healthiest stem. Although this sprout will have a crook at its base for a few years, it will usually turn into a straight, fast-growing tree.

TOOLS

Woodlot management does not require a large investment in terms of tools. Time and effort are much more important than fancy tools. A small woodlot can be kept in top shape with only a chain saw, an ax, and a pruning saw. A selection of the right tools does make the work a lot easier.

The chain saw is one of the most useful and efficient tools in woodlot management, figure 3−9. It is used in pruning large or injured limbs, felling trees, cutting logs to manageable lengths, as well as cutting up firewood. Most brand-name saws work well with reasonable care. Features to look for include a 14−20 inch (35−50 cm) bar with sprocket nose, vibration-free handles, and a chain guard or brake. Safety equipment to use with a chain saw includes goggles, ear protection, and a hard hat. Hard hats should be used whenever working in the woods, since even a small branch

loosened by vibration and falling a long distance can cause injury. Safety helmets with face shields and ear protectors are now available as a single unit. Sturdy, comfortable boots with steel toes are recommended footwear.

The ax, although much slower than the chain saw, is still useful in the woods (figure 3−10). From felling and branch removal to clearing shrubs around trees, the ax is useful, light, inexpensive, and versatile. A 2½−4

3−8. Oaks, sprouting from a stump. Three of the four trunks should be cut.

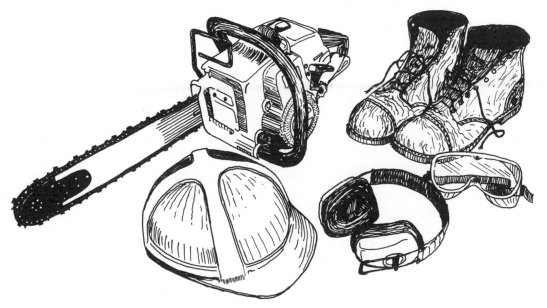

3−9. Chain saw and safety equipment: helmet, ear protectors, goggles, and steel-toed boots.

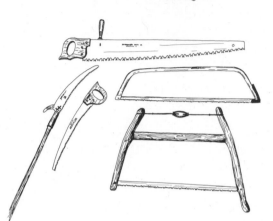

3–10. *Top,* felling axe; *middle,* splitting maul; *bottom,* wedge.

3–11. Various saws, clockwise from top: one-man crosscut, metal-frame bucksaw, wood bucksaw, hand pruning saw, and pole pruner.

3–12. Lopping shears and hand pruner.

3–13. Peavy, or cant hook, and timber carrier.

3–14. Measuring tools: board rule, timber cruiser stick, and tape.

pound (1.1–1.8 kg) head is about the right weight. Double-bitted heads are for experts only. Wedges are also useful. Splitting mauls should be used for splitting firewood.

Saws come in a variety of styles (figure 3–11). Handsaws can be either rigid or the folding type. Pole pruning saws allow overhead work without the use of ladders. These saws have coarse teeth with extra "set" to prevent binding in green wood. They are used for cutting off small branches only. The larger handsaws can be used for felling or log and firewood cutting. The one-man crosscut saws with blades of 3–4 feet (.9–1.2 m) do an excellent job, although they are a bit more tiring than the chain saw. The old bucksaws or the newer tension framed saws with replaceable blades can also be used for cutting trees to about the pole stage, as well as for pruning and thinning work. These small, inexpensive saws cut surprisingly fast.

Lopping shears are used for quick cutting of small branches, seedlings, and small saplings. They are relatively inexpensive, yet can tackle branches up to 2 inches (5 cm) because of the leverage exerted by the long handles (figure 3–12). For small pruning jobs, a pair of hand pruners is less tiring since it can be used one-handed.

Logs, once cut, can be moved or positioned for further cutting or loading using a peavy or cant hook (or dog). These long-handled tools with swinging hooks make it easy to grab and roll logs of considerable size into position (figure 3–13). Timber carriers, which look like ice tongs with a long handle, are used by two people to lift and drag logs of small and medium size.

The cruiser stick or log rule is a tool not often mentioned in books for the small-woodlot owner. It is usually used by foresters, timber scalers, and sawyers. There are several types (figure 3–14). The timber cruiser stick helps estimate the timber in standing trees. It consists of up to four scales: two reflect inches and tree diameter; another, a Merritt Hypsometer scale, determines tree height (by holding the stick vertically at arm's length a predetermined distance from the tree); and finally a log scale determines the estimated number of board feet in a log or tree of a specified length. Regular log rules are used by sawyers at the mill to determine the number of board feet in each log as it is unloaded. By knowing the length of the logs and measuring the average diameter of the small (top) end inside the bark, one can read the total number of board feet in that log off the corresponding column. These log rules are based on several different formulas (Doyle, Scribner, Scribner Decimal C, International, etc.), which take into account the amount of taper in the log and various methods of sawing the same log, and thereby arrive at a "guestimate" of the actual wood volume, measured in board feet. By using these log rules, the woodlot owner can determine in advance the amount of wood he has in a given tree, in a pile of harvested logs, or on a certain amount of land. A good tape is useful in measuring exact circumference and log length.

PRUNING

Like thinning, some pruning occurs naturally in the forest but, again, at a very slow, inefficient rate. As the trees grow upward in competition for light, the lower branches eventually die and fall off. This process can take years and results in low-grade lumber, since the wood grows around the dead branch or stub and results in a long black knot. When branches are broken off by wind, the stubs will often be 3–12 inches (7.5–30 cm) or longer. To cover a stub of this length can require decades.

Pruning by the landowner is therefore the alternative. Branches should be pruned as soon as they die. If the cut is made cleanly and close

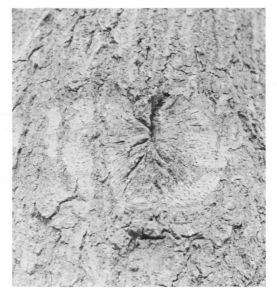

3–15. Healed pruned knot.

to the trunk, the wound can heal over in three to eight years (figure 3–15), depending on the size of the branch cut. Figure 3–16 shows a knot in a board that was pruned and grew over in a few years. Although the branch was fairly large to begin with, it healed rapidly and created only a small defect in the board. Figure 3–17, on the other hand, shows a branch that was not pruned. Had it been pruned at the point where it turns from a solid, red knot to a loose black (or dead) knot, the wood from that point on would have been clear.

Pruning is a rather laborious process, but

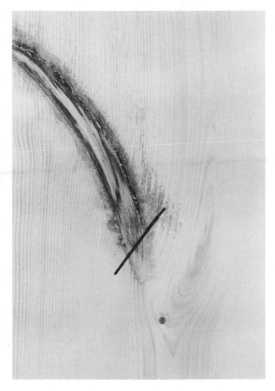

3–16 *(left).* Large, pruned, and overgrown knot.

3–17 *(right).* Slash knot that should have been pruned years ago.

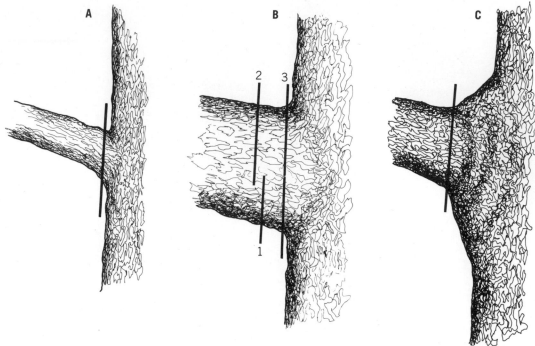

3–18. (A) The majority of branches are pruned flush to the trunk. (B) Large branches are removed with three cuts. (C) Some hardwoods with "collars" are pruned away from the trunk.

one that pays dividends both visually and economically. In one morning a stand of scrubby, overgrown trees can be turned into a stand of clear, straight trunks. Once a pruning program is well under way, the yearly maintenance pruning goes much faster. Economically, clear wood of almost any species is worth two to three times as much as its knotty counterpart.

3–19. Ax-pruned branches leave ragged stubs that take extra years to heal.

There are a few rules to keep in mind when pruning:

1. Use sharp tools to maximize efficiency of cutting and minimize tearing of the woody tissue.

2. To eliminate tearing of the bark below the cut, saw very large branches in three cuts, as in figure 3–18(B). First, make a cut a distance from the trunk, underneath the branch. Second, make another cut slightly outward from the first and on the top side of the branch in order to drop the branch. Finally, with the weight of the branch gone, make the third cut flush to the trunk. All pruning should be flush to the trunk to minimize healing time. Finger-sized branches can be removed in a single cut.

3. Avoid using axes and hatchets. An ax cut can injure the bark when swung too close or leave a ragged stump when cut too far from the trunk (figure 3–19).

4. Start pruning as early as possible to assure a maximum amount of clear wood in the trunk. The early sapling stage is ideal. Prune only about 200 of the best and straightest trees per acre. It is usually not worthwhile to start a pruning program when most of the trees are in the late pole or early standard stage. Too much of the trunk consists of knots at that stage, while some of the branches will likely be quite large. Live branches larger than 2 inches in diameter (5 cm) should not be cut.

5. Cut all dead branches, regardless of size.

6. Prune a tree up to two-thirds of its total height. A minimum of one-third its height must be left in live branches.

7. Cut dead branches at any time of the year, but leave cutting live ones to late fall and early winter. Avoid pruning species such as the maples in late winter, since the cuts will bleed sap in early spring.

8. When pruning (or thinning), cut up the shorn branches and waste (slash)—especially the larger ones—to minimize the volume and bring it all in contact with the ground, thereby speeding up the decay process and reducing the fire danger. Figure 3-20 shows a newly pruned stand of planted pine.

DISEASE AND PEST CONTROL
Disease is rare in a healthy, clean, well-thinned, and pruned woodlot. Diseases are caused by organisms such as viruses, fungi, and bacteria, and are usually grouped into categories of heart rot, root diseases, rusts, blights, and wilts.

Insect damage is usually more noticeable. Insects are grouped by the method in which they do damage:

1. *Terminal feeders* are larvae of adult moths, weevils, or beetles, which feed on the leading shoots and terminal buds of trees. Most of their damage causes deformities, especially in conifers.

2. *Defoliators* are usually the larvae of moths, sawflies, or beetles. They eat needles and leaves, and can strip acres at a time if not controlled. A defoliated tree becomes weakened and may die if the defoliation continues for several years.

3. *Bark borers* do most of their damage by burrowing under the bark and actually eating the cambium layer. They leave characteristic maps or engravings in the cambium and can kill the tree if the cambium is girdled all the way around.

4. *Wood borers* are larvae of adult beetles (or carpenter ants and termites, which attack dry wood). They seldom kill the tree since they do most of their damage in the heartwood and sapwood. The wood they feed on is, however, often ruined.

5. *Root feeders* are usually problems only with seedlings and do not bother mature trees to any large extent.

6. *Sucking insects* such as aphids and scales suck fluids from the soft parts of trees, thereby weakening them. Again, they cause more of a problem with young trees but seldom kill them.

7. *Seed borers* deposit their eggs in the seeds, where the larvae hatch and destroy the seed. No direct damage to the tree occurs; however, they destroy fruits and nuts and can make natural reseeding difficult.

8. *Gall makers*—the wasps, mites, midges, or aphids—produce abnormal growths on leaves, stems, or trunks. These deformities seldom cause extensive damage to the tree or the wood.

Early detection and treatment of diseases and insects make their control much easier. The identification and treatment of the multitudes of diseases and insects is beyond the scope of this book. A professional forester or arborist should be consulted for specifics.

REPLANTING
Idle land or acreage not suited for agriculture can be replanted in trees. As stated previously, depending on the species planted, it usually requires 40–100 years until harvest. In most cases the person doing the planting is not the one to benefit from the rewards. However, a prime woodlot, pruned and cared for, increases in value with each year.

Planting a large area is a slow and exacting process that must be done with care. Certain rules should be followed to assure success of the project:

1. Be sure to designate the planting site

3–20. Beginning of a pruning operation. The slash is trampled low to the ground to speed decay and reduce fire danger.

as a woodlot and protect it from changes in land use. A landowner must be committed to maintaining the land as a woodlot for several decades.

2. Select species native to the area. This assures that the species are adapted to the general climate and growing conditions. It is better to plant a mixture of several compatible species, since this diversity provides a more natural forest and offers better resistance to disease and insect attacks.

3. Perform soil tests to determine soil pH and fertility and to better match the species to be planted to the soil type. If the soil is extremely poor, it may be necessary to add organic matter, lime, trace minerals, or an all-purpose fertilizer.

4. Make sure seedlings are healthy and fresh and roots are kept moist at all times.

5. Provide follow-up care. Check the planting for insects and disease; cut weeds and competing vegetation; and prune and thin as the trees become older.

For planting on a small scale (a few acres or less), use a spade or a planting bar, which looks like a very thin spade. Thrust the bar into the ground and move it forward and back once or twice. In the resulting deep, narrow hole, insert the seedling. Remove the bar and thrust it into the soil 2−3 inches (5−7.5 cm) behind the hole. Next, pull it backwards to close the bottom of the hole. Then push it forward to close the top of the hole. Remove the bar and partially close the second hole with your heel as you move to the next location. This procedure will assure that there are no air pockets around the roots. With practice, the entire process takes only seconds, and an experienced planter can set up to 1,500 seedlings per day.

Many nurseries specialize in seedlings for reforestation. They offer both conifers and deciduous trees in either one-, two-, or three-year-old seedlings in lots of 100 or 1,000 at reasonable prices. These seedlings are usually 6−24 inches high (15−60 cm) and shipped with bare roots (wrapped in sawdust and plastic to keep them moist).

PROFESSIONAL HELP

All types of help are available to the woodlot owner who takes the time and energy to seek it out. Both state and federal agencies, as well as private organizations, can offer direct help or at least send pamphlets, literature and how-to guides.

The U.S. Government Printing Office produces a wide variety of literature available at a nominal fee. (Write to Superintendent of Documents, U.S. Government Printing Office, Washington, D.C. 20402.) Several federal agencies are set up specifically to aid the landowner, woodlot owner, and/or farmer. The Department of Agriculture's Agricultural Stabilization and Conservation Service (ASCS) offers a forestry incentive program. (Contact Department of Agriculture, Fourteenth Street and Independence Avenue S.W., Washington, D.C. 20250.) The U.S. Forest Service, also part of the Department of Agriculture, conducts research in the entire field of forestry and makes it available to any citizen. Its Soil Conservation Service (SCS) provides technical assistance and resource data to land users in rural areas. The SCS also helps finance small watershed protection programs and helps with the improvement of wildlife habitat. Through its cooperative program, the SCS will send a local agent to analyze the soil type, make suggestions as to the best land use, and draw up a land use plan complete with aerial photo.

On the state level, the services offered are often more direct and personal. Each state department or bureau of forestry usually has state foresters who will actually assist the woodlot owner in marking trees for thinning and removal, make suggestions as to better management practices, and lead the landowner to any other services available. The Cooperative Extension Service (a service of the U.S. Department of Agriculture) is administered through the state land grant colleges, as well as other local offices. Their basic service is to make available the results of research from all federal agencies and land grant institutions to landowners, users, or processors (as well as youth groups, farmers, homemakers, etc.).

There are also numerous private organizations of interest to the woodlot manager. The American Forest Institute (1619 Massachusetts Avenue, N.W., Washington, D.C. 20036) and the American Forestry Association (1319 Eighteenth Street, N.W., Washington, D.C. 20036) are just two of these, dedicated to the wise management of the forest. A complete listing of the addresses of all American and Canadian government departments, agencies, bureaus, and offices concerned with conservation, as well as state and provincial, international, national, interstate, private organizations, and citizens groups can be found in the Conservation Directory published yearly by the National Wildlife Federation, 1412 Sixteenth Street, N.W., Washington, DC 20036.

HARVESTING

Harvest can start at any time. The initial thinning operation can produce cords of firewood. To the landowner who has spent years cutting, thinning, pruning, and caring for his woodlot, harvest means cutting trees that go to the sawmill. After years of patience and work, the reward is a neatly stacked pile of lumber.

Most cutting is done in the fall or winter. At that time the leaves are off the trees, assuring more light and better visibility. Fall is usually drier, and by winter the ground is frozen in the north, providing better footing for man and machine. Not only is the traction better, but less energy is required to skid logs over frozen or dry ground as opposed to mud. Besides, topsoil is a precious commodity in the forest, and it is worth the landowner's while to protect it; ruts left by the tracks of heavy machines form gullies during the next wet season, and the resulting erosion causes considerable damage to logging roads and the forest soil.

CUTTING ALTERNATIVES

Several methods of cutting are available to the woodlot manager. These include the selection method, the shelter wood system, the seed tree system, and clear cutting. Each has its advantages and disadvantages, which should be weighed in order to derive the maximum benefit from the woodlot.

The *selection method* is probably best for the small woodlot, especially if it is a mixed-age stand. It consists of selecting and cutting only the mature trees, usually only a few per acre per year. The gaps left by the harvested trees allow for the growth of the smaller trees in the understory. Thus, by harvesting only a few trees per year and encouraging the growth of the other trees, a continuous or sustained yield of trees is assured over the life of the management program. The financial returns are small but are like a yearly dividend. The system also lends itself well to the small woodlot in that it does not require any heavy equipment, since only a relatively small amount of wood is harvested at once.

The *shelter wood system* can also be used on a small woodlot. It consists of a series of cuts that let light in gradually. Enough trees are left to protect or shelter the new growth until it becomes established. First, a preparatory cut is made to open the canopy and encourage seed production. This removes about 25 percent of the stand. Next, a cutting is made that removes about 75 percent of the remaining trees and allows more sun and space for the seedlings. Finally, when the growth is well established, the removal cut can be made in stages (selectively) or as one cut. Care must be exercised not to damage the new crop during this cut. This method condenses the financial returns over a few years, allows for natural reseeding, and assures that the forest is never left bare.

The *seed tree system* is a simplified form of the shelter wood system. Most of the timber is harvested during an initial cutting that leaves only about four or six of the healthiest, most wind-firm trees per acre. These trees are left to reseed the area and are cut when the seedlings become well established. This method works best on even-aged stands. It brings the bulk of the financial returns after the first cutting, and the remaining within a few years.

Clear cutting, as the name implies, involves the removal of all growth from a given area. Smaller trees not sold as timber can be sold as pulp or firewood. Clear cutting lends itself well to larger operations because of its efficiency. It works best on even-aged stands. Small clear-cut areas can reseed naturally, whereas larger ones must be reseeded manually or replanted, at which point a change of species is possible. It gives a one-time financial return but requires decades between harvests. Since it is used most often on large operations, it usually involves heavy machinery, which leads to erosion problems on the freshly bared soil.

METHODS OF HARVEST

Here again the landowner has a choice of equipment in removing wood from the forest. Two considerations are obvious in determining the type of equipment to be used: finances at hand and the size of the area to be harvested. It would be foolish to invest $35,000 on a skidder for a fifteen-acre woodlot. The equipment must fit not only the budget but also the size of the job.

The least expensive method of harvesting is to do it by hand, using timber tongs and/or a hand winch. Tongs are used by two people to

3–21. Horse logging, though slower than using a skidder, is much easier on the forest soil.

3–22. The Quadractor, a useful low-cost tractor for the small-woodlot owner. (courtesy, Traction, Inc.)

most areas, and the winch is used as a backup to retrieve logs in ravines or from steep banks. Farm tractors can be used for the same purpose. In rural areas it is often possible to rent this equipment.

For larger operations it might be advisable to hire someone with the right equipment to not only skid the logs out of the woods, but also to do the actual cutting. Independent woods operators can be found in most locations where logging is practiced. They have their own equipment and know how to use it safely and efficiently. Those who own skidders usually work the fastest, at the least expensive rate. Skidders are large four-wheel-drive diesel tractors, often hinged in the middle for maneuverability, with a small blade in the front for pushing obstacles and a towing winch in the back for pulling logs.

Because of its size and weight, the machine not only leaves deep ruts in soft soil but is also damaging to seedlings, saplings, and the bark of larger trees unless it is operated with extreme care. For this reason there has been a revival in the last few years of the small woods operator logging with horses. Many landowners prefer the quieter, less damaging job done with these animals (figure 3–21). Although logging with horses takes longer and costs more, the better condition of the woodlot after the operation is completed usually makes it worthwhile.

A more recent innovation is the Quadractor (figure 3–22). Designed and built by an aircraft engineer in North Troy, Vermont, the Quadractor has such features as a flexible frame, 31-inch (78 cm) ground clearance, and four-wheel drive and steering that gives it a zero turning radius. Its light weight (about 900 pound or 410 kg) and low-pressure tires exert less weight per square inch than a man walking. Other tractors derive their traction from sheer mass and yet they can barely pull their own weight. The Quadractor "borrows" the weight of its load for traction, so the 900-pound machine can pull up to 4,000 pounds (1,800 kg). This is accomplished with a 72:1 gear ratio and an 8-horsepower Briggs and Stratton engine. All this for less than the price of a garden tractor.

Another method of harvesting timber is by cable logging. This involves cables stretched between trees along previously cleared corridors. Using a winch, logs can be dragged to a central landing and loading yard, minimizing the need for an extensive road network. Until recently,

lift and drag one end of a log. This works perfectly well for the pole-stage trees or even shorter lengths of standard-stage lengths of trees. This method is best suited for the harvest of firewood or thinned trees. For larger timbers it has obvious drawbacks.

Most small operators use an all-terrain vehicle or a four-wheel-drive pickup truck and a winch. This works best if the woodlot has a few woods roads running through it. Four-wheel-drive trucks can be maneuvered into this system was used primarily on large timber operations, especially out west and in areas of rough terrain. Now, several Canadian and European manufacturers are marketing small-scale cable systems. A firm in New England even has a model small enough for firewood harvest.

OTHER SOURCES OF WOOD

What about the woodworker who does not have access to a woodlot? Is he destined to forever purchase from lumberyards or sawmills where high price and low selection are the rule? There are a few alternatives available to those willing to search them out. The firewood pile is a wonderful place for finding chunks of cherry, beech, walnut, or figured maple. If firewood dealers are in the area, they may sell a few 4-foot (1.2 m) lengths at reasonable prices. Another suggestion is to seek out land clearing operations. These usually involve tree removal; since most construction companies, whether highway or building, are not in the business of selling wood, the "waste" is usually bulldozed to the side and burned. Permission from the foreman and an afternoon spent with a chain saw will result in a good pile of usable timber, ready to saw and dry.

Any good-sized wood manufacturing operation, from a cabinet shop to a furniture manufacturing plant to a turning mill, will have waste wood. This is either thrown out, burned, or sold for a nominal fee. The wood is usually quite high quality, kiln dried, and top grade. Most of the scrap available is in short lengths. Turning mills can be a gold mine for figured wood. Automatic lathes have trouble with such figured wood as maple and birch, which will therefore be regarded as "defective."

Public and private tree crews and arborists have wood they either give away or sell. These crews cut rights of way for powerlines and cut damaged, diseased, or dangerous trees as well as remove windfalls. Getting in touch with these tree service companies can yield dividends in the form of an occasional trunk of pine, Osage orange, sycamore, or birch. In some towns and counties, the public tree crews will leave their cuttings in firewood lengths by the side of the roads, free for the taking. In some areas, adjacent land owners have first right to the wood cut by public tree crews.

CHAPTER 4

SAWING AND DRYING WOOD

SAWING

Finding a sawmill is not always an easy matter. In urban sections of the country and in areas where forestry is not a common business, sawmills may be scarce and difficult to locate. They can be found in the Yellow Pages of the telephone directory under "Mills," "Sawmills," or "Lumber—Retail/Wholesale." A better method is to contact your state's Department of Forestry or Forest Resources, which probably publishes a listing of all sawmills in the state. These listings include not only locations and phone numbers, but also the size of the mill (thousands of board feet processed yearly), mill type (custom sawing, long lumber, veneer, cooperage, fencing, shingles, etc.), equipment at the mill (bandsaws, overhead saws, debarkers, kilns, planers, or molders), and species processed (softwoods only, hardwoods only, mixed species, or single species). Some state forestry departments, especially those in heavy timber-producing states, also publish lists of secondary wood producers. These would include plywood manufacturers; furniture manufacturers; cabinet shops; millworks producing molding, doors, and windows; turning mills; container and pallet manufacturers; and makers of toys and novelties.

After you have located a few mills, it is a good idea to check the quality of the cutting and call around for prices. Custom sawing varies, depending on the amount, the species, and often on the sawyer himself. The price also depends on whether or not the lumber is planed after sawing, or even kiln dried. Most mills have a fixed price per thousand board feet; others will take a percentage of lumber sawn. Obviously the percentage of pine kept by the sawyer will be higher than the percentage of walnut. The labor is about the same, yet the finished lumber varies tremendously in price. Some mills will charge more for sawing extra-hard wood such as black locust, dogwood, or Osage orange, since these woods dull sawteeth quickly. Sawyers will often ask if the logs were cut from a backyard or fence row, out of concern for hidden nails and spikes. Others will require a blade deposit against possible damage.

Prior to taking logs to the mill, it is a good idea to paint the ends of logs with a heavy oil paint. This serves a dual purpose: first, to seal the end grain to prevent too-rapid drying and checking; and second, to identify the logs by color, especially if odd colors are used. This recommendation does not imply that sawmill operators are dishonest; it just makes the job of identification easier for everyone.

METHODS OF CUTTING

There are two general methods of sawing lumber, plainsawn or flat-sawn, and quartersawn or rift-sawn (figure 4–1). Plainsawn wood is by far the cheaper, more common, and more readily available. Some sawmills will not even attempt to quartersaw.

Plainsawn (in hardwood) or flat-sawn (in

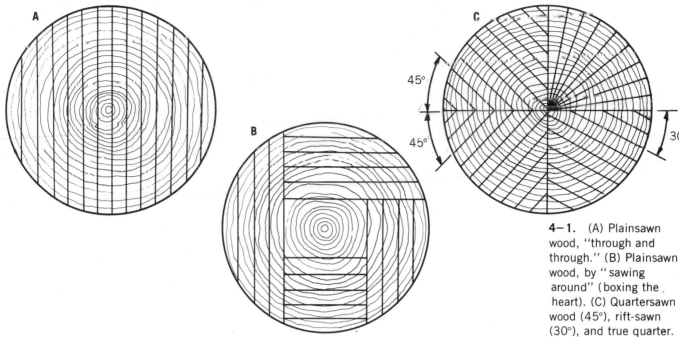

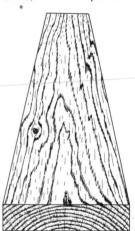

4—1. (A) Plainsawn wood, "through and through." (B) Plainsawn wood, by "sawing around" (boxing the heart). (C) Quartersawn wood (45°), rift-sawn (30°), and true quarter.

softwood), as the name suggests, is a relatively simple method by which the log is passed through the blade in the same position until it is completely sawn into boards. A variation, called sawing around, involves cutting until defects are encountered, then turning the log 90°. Plainsawing is cheapest and most efficient because it involves very little rotation of the log during the cutting process and leaves very little waste. By definition, flat-sawing means that the angle of the growth rings is between 0° and 45° to the wide surface of the board. This results in the wide-figure patterns seen on the faces of plainsawn lumber (figure 4—2). To some, this pattern is much more attractive than quartersawn wood. Knots, when present, are round or oval; thus the board is stronger than a quartersawn board (which usually has spike knots across the entire face of the board). Plainsawn wood is less likely to collapse in the kiln and shrinks and swells less in thickness.

Quartersawn (in hardwoods) or vertical- or edge-sawn (in softwoods) is a little more complex. The log is first sawn in half, longitudinally, then each half is again sawn in half, resulting in four equal quarters (see figure 4—1). These are then tipped on their points (the pith or center of the log) and sawn in one of several ways. Most commonly, the quarter is just sawn through and through, with the blade at 45° to the two flat edges of the quarter and all saw cuts parallel to each other. An older and more difficult method is to set one flat edge of the quarter almost parallel to the blade and then cut

a series of thin, pie-shaped boards. This involves repositioning the log after each cut so that the blade passes through the point of the quarter each time. Old clapboards were almost always sawn this way. Rift-sawing, a variation of quartersawing, means that the flat sides of the quarter pass at 30° and 60° to the saw blade. True quartersawn wood has the growth rings at an angle of 60° to 90° to the wide face of the board. Rift-sawn wood has the growth rings running 30° to 60° to the wide face. Quartersawn wood lacks the large figure pattern of plainsawn wood. Instead, it shows a series of parallel lines, the edges of the growth rings (figure 4—3). Species with conspicuous and long rays, such as oak, form a beautiful fleck pattern, (figure 4—4). The biggest advantage of quartersawn wood is that there is almost no cupping or twisting and only a minimum of shrinking and swelling across its width. There is

4—2. Plainsawn board.

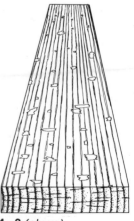

4—3 *(above).* Quartersawn board.

4—4 *(left).* Quartersawn oak with ray flecks.

usually less surface checking, and raised grain caused by ring separation is less pronounced. In use, it wears more evenly and holds paint and finishes better, depending on the species. Sapwood is confined to one edge of the board, and is limited to the width of the sapwood in the log.

A close look at the plainsawn lumber in figure 4–1 shows that if the wood is sawn through and through, a few boards next to as well as above and below the pith will be quartersawn, since the sawblade passes almost directly through the center of the log at this point.

When to use quartersawn or plainsawn wood? Quartersawn is preferred under circumstances in which warp, shrinkage, and expansion must be kept to a minimum and when wear is an important factor. For example, quartersawn wood is preferred in floors where the boards are subject to wear and must remain flat, and where the gaps between them must be kept as small as possible. Quartersawn wood is also ideal for clapboards, where warping, shrinkage, and expansion must be minimized, as well as for door frames, any frame construction, and unsupported shelves or breadboards. On the other hand, when the appearance of the wide, flowing figure of plainsawn wood is desired and the wood is properly restrained to prevent warpage, plainsawn wood is the proper choice. For panels in frames, case sides, drawer fronts, and even tabletops, as long as the wood is given room to move (as in a frame and panel) and supported to prevent warping (as in a dovetailed corner), plainsaw wood is fine.

Since plainsawn lumber is much cheaper, more common, and easier to find, quartersawn wood cannot always be used where it best suits. Out of necessity, any available lumber must therefore be substituted. Allowances must be made to provide for shrinkage and expansion. See chapter 5, "Compensating for Shrinkage and Expansion."

GRADING LUMBER

Hardwood is graded into three categories, depending on its use and market: finished market products, dimension parts, and factory grades. Finished market products are cut and graded at the mill in their finished form; there is little or no remanufacturing involved. These products include flooring (by far the largest volume), siding, ties, lath, construction boards, trim, molding, stair treads, and risers. Both dimension parts and factory grades are intended for re-

manufacture. The difference is that dimension parts are graded on overall clarity, while factory grades reflect the proportion of a piece that can be cut into useful smaller pieces. Factory-graded lumber is most commonly available at lumberyards and is also sold to furniture manufacturers. Consequently, the grading for this type of lumber is the most important for the woodworker. Rules for grading are those established by the National Hardwood Lumber Association. The grades, from best to worst follow: Firsts and Seconds (FAS), Selects (Sel), Number 1 Common, Number 2 Common, Number 3A Common, and Number 3B Common. The standards for each grade are quite complex and include allowable minimum width and length, and the number of cuttings allowed per board to produce a given percentage of clear wood. For example, FAS has a minimum allowable width of 6 inches (15 cm) and a minimum length of 8 feet (2.4 m). The board can be cut up to three times, depending on the length, and must yield 91⅔ percent clear wood, with a minimum cutting size. On the other hand, Number 3B Common lumber has a minimum width of 3 inches (7.5 cm) and a minimum length of 4 feet (1.2 m). The board can be cut an unlimited number of times to produce a clarity of only 25 percent. Defects taken into consideration when counting the number of cuttings include knots, checks, wane, bark, rot, and insect damage. Sapwood is not considered a defect. A complete listing of standards for each grade is shown in figure 4–5.

The grading of softwood is a different story. There are nine or more private organizations, each of which sets standards for one or more species of softwoods. For example, both the Northeastern Lumber Manufacturers Association, Inc., and the Northern Hardwood and Pine Manufacturers Association set standards for white pine. In general, softwood lumber is divided into construction lumber and lumber for remanufacture.

Construction lumber consists of stress-graded, nonstress-graded, and appearance lumber. Stress-graded lumber is 2 inches (5 cm) and thicker, and is graded not to appearance but for strength. It is used for studs, joists, posts, beams, and stringers. Nonstress-graded lumber is used for siding, shelving, paneling, and subflooring. Grades in this category are No. 1, No. 2, No. 3. Appearance lumber is graded for appearance only, not structural integrity.

4–5. Standard Hardwood Cutting Grades[1]

Grade and lengths allowed (feet)	Widths allowed	Surface measure of pieces	Amount of each piece that must work into clear-face cuttings	Maximum cuttings allowed	Minimum size of cuttings required
	In.	Sq. ft.	%	Number	
Firsts:[2] 8 to 16 (will admit 30 percent of 8- to 11-foot, ½ of which may be 8- and 9-foot.)	6+	4 to 9	91⅔	1	4 inches by 5 feet, or 3 inches by 7 feet
		10 to 14	91⅔	2	
		15+	91⅔	3	
Seconds:[2] 8 to 16 (will admit 30 percent of 8- to 11-foot, ½ of which may be 8- and 9-foot).	6+	4 and 5	83⅓	1	Do.
		6 and 7	83⅓	1	
		6 and 7	91⅔	2	
		8 to 11	83⅓	2	
		8 to 11	91⅔	3	
		12 to 15	83½	3	
		12 to 15	91⅔	4	
		16+	83⅓	4	
Selects: 6 to 16 (will admit 30 percent of 6- to 11-foot, 1/6 of which may be 6- and 7-foot).	4+	2 and 3	91⅔	1	Do.
		4+	see[3]		
No. 1 Common: 4 to 16 (will admit 10 percent of 4- to 7-foot, ½ of which may be 4- and 5-foot).	3+	1	100	0	4 inches by 2 feet, or 3 inches by 3 feet
		2	75	1	
		3 and 4	66⅔	1	
		3 and 4	75	2	
		5 to 7	66⅔	2	
		5 to 7	75	3	
		8 to 10	66⅔	3	
		11 to 13	66⅔	4	
		14+	66⅔	5	
No. 2 Common: 4 to 16 (will admit 30 percent of 4- to 7-foot, ⅓ of which may be 4- and 5-foot).	3+	1	66⅔	1	3 inches by 2 feet
		2 and 3	50	1	
		2 and 3	66⅔	2	
		4 and 5	50	2	
		4 and 5	66⅔	3	
		6 and 7	50	3	
		6 and 7	66⅔	4	
		8 and 9	50	4	
		10 and 11	50	5	
		12 and 13	50	6	
		14+	50	7	
No. 3A Common: 4 to 16 (will admit 50 percent of 4- to 7-foot, ½ of which may be 4- and 5-foot).	3+	1+	[4]33⅓	see[5]	Do.
No. 3B Common: 4 to 16 (will admit 50 percent of 4- to 7-foot, ½ of which may be 4- and 5-foot).	3+	1+	[6]25	see[5]	1½ inches by 2 feet

[1]Inspection to be made on the poorer side of the piece, except in Selects.

[2]Firsts and Seconds are combined as 1 grade (FAS). The percentage of Firsts required in the combined grade varies from 20 to 40 percent, depending on the species.

[3]Same as Seconds with reverse side of board not below No. 1 Common or reverse side of cuttings sound.

[4]This grade also admits pieces that grade not below No. 2 Common on the good face and have the reverse face sound.

[5]Unlimited.

[6]The cuttings must be sound; clear face not required.

Source: U.S. Forest Products Laboratory, *Wood Handbook.*

Graded B and Better, C and Better, and D, it is used for finish work, trim, flooring, ceiling, casing, and built-in cabinet work.

Lumber for remanufacture is composed of several categories, each with its own rules and standards. These include factory or shop grades, industrial clears, structural laminations, and various other standards for molding, ladders, tank, pole, and pencil stock.

For the small-woodlot owner who uses his own stock, these rules are of no real consequence. To anyone cutting and sawing for resale, however, as well as the woodworker purchasing wood from a mill or lumberyard, the rules covering the specific wood type should be known and understood.

OWNER-OPERATED SAWMILLS

Rather than hauling the wood to the local sawmill, the woodworker with a sizable woodlot has the option of operating his own mill. Several varieties are on the market, from inexpensive chain saw attachments to large permanent mills running to several thousand dollars.

Chain saw units are the least expensive and the most portable. The smallest units attach to any chainsaw, ride on a flat plank, and cost under $100. These small units are good for sawing a few logs a day. At the other end of the spectrum are the two-man chain saw mills, with two saw motors, rollers, and guides, which cost up to several thousand dollars. These larger units have a much higher rate of production. Two experienced operators can turn out several

4—6. Ross Bandmill: close-up of carriage and log brackets. (courtesy, Weinrebe/W.K. Ross, Inc.)

thousand board feet a day. There are drawbacks to any chain saw mill. First, special chains are required for the ripping operation. Because of the thickness of the blade and chain, the saw kerf is usually ⅜ inch (.9 cm), meaning more waste per cut. Since the mill passes through the log, it means the operators work in a bent-over position, resulting in backaches. So while the mill may be capable of sawing several thousand feet of lumber a day, the operators cannot continue this on a daily basis.

One of the most popular of the stationary mills is the Belsaw one-man sawmill. This mill, with its 40-inch (1 m) circular blade, can handle logs up to 18 inches (45 cm) in diameter and 14 feet (4.3 m) long. It cuts with speed and efficiency. The controls are easy to operate and are located away from the blade. The mill costs several thousand dollars and does not include a power source (25 horsepower minimum required) or a base.

The most recent entry in the one-man sawmill field is the Ross Portable Bandmill (figure 4–6). This mill reflects a totally new approach, utilizing existing technology. A horizontally mounted bandsaw with a one-inch (2.5 cm) blade, powered by a 5-horsepower engine, is mounted on a dolly and rides along a 20-foot (6.1 m) piece of solid channel iron. Logs are rolled onto the holder, and the saw cuts through the wood at a rate of 8 to 12 square feet per minute. Replacement blades are inexpensive, should nails be encountered in the wood. The kerf is only ¹/16 inch (1.8 mm), which means much less wood is wasted as sawdust. By alternately shimming opposite sides of a plank, clapboards can be produced. The mill has a capacity of 17.5 inches (44 cm) by about 19 feet (5.8 m) and can cut a maximum thickness of 4.25 inches (10.8 cm) down to a minimum of about ¹/16 inch (1.8 mm). The operation is quiet and simple, and the finished boards are extremely smooth. The mill can be skidded behind a truck or tractor directly to the work site.

DRYING WOOD

Freshly cut or green wood is not suitable for most woodworking purposes. Green wood can be used for rough construction such as barns and buildings, shingles, baskets, and even certain types of chair construction. For use in furniture, trim, or built-ins, however, wood must be dried first. There are several reasons why dry wood is more suitable than green wood. First, a large percentage of the shrinkage from the green to the dry condition can be eliminated by drying wood to the correct moisture content (M.C.). The first-time shrinkage from wet wood to 8% or 10% M.C. is usually the greatest, so any warping that may result occurs before the wood is worked into a finished product. Drying brings the wood into equilibrium with the moisture present in the air. Second, drying reduces stain and mold since most stain-causing fungi cannot live below a certain moisture level. Third, drying reduces weight. One of the reasons that construction lumber is kiln dried is to save freight costs. The weight of 1,000 board feet of rock maple goes from 5,400 pounds (2,450 kg) green weight to 3,000 pounds (1,360 kg) at 6% moisture content. And, finally, wet wood will not take a finish. Preservatives, oil finishes, and surface finishes will not penetrate or grab the wood. Paint will not hold and will blister in a short time.

The amount of moisture present in wood differs not only among species, but also between heartwood and sapwood and is affected by position in tree and time of year (figure 4–7). The green moisture content varies from about 44% in the sapwood of white ash to over 200% in the sapwood of western red cedar, sugar pine, and redwood. These percentages are based on *oven-dried weight* of the wood. Thus, the weight of the green sapwood of redwood is two-thirds water and one-third actual wood.

FREE AND BOUND WATER

Water in wood is present in two forms: free and bound. *Free water* is that which is located in the cell cavities and between cells. It is the first to evaporate, the easiest to remove, and in no way affects the cell structure of the wood. The point at which all of the free water has evaporated from the wood is termed the *fiber saturation point*. The cell cavities are now empty, but the wood fibers are still saturated. Wood at the fiber saturation point has a moisture content of between 25% and 30%.

The remaining water, the *bound water*, consists of water molecules held tightly within the cell walls but not part of the wood material. Removing bound water requires energy. Once the water molecules are loosened and begin to evaporate, the cell walls and the wood itself begin to shrink. Shrinkage and swelling of wood are caused by changes in moisture content.

If all of the free water were to evaporate

4–7. Average Moisture Content of Green Wood, by Species

Species	Moisture content[1] Heartwood Pct.	Sapwood Pct.
HARDWOODS		
Apple	81	74
Ash, white	46	44
Basswood, American	81	133
Beech, American	55	72
Birch, yellow	74	72
Cherry, black	58	—
Chestnut, American	120	—
Elm, American	95	92
Hickory, true, pignut	71	49
Maple, sugar	65	72
Oak, northern red	80	69
southern red	83	75
water	81	81
white	64	78
willow	82	74
Sweetgum	79	137
Sycamore, American	114	130
Walnut, black	90	73
Yellow-poplar	83	106
SOFTWOODS		
Bald cypress	121	171
Cedar, eastern red cedar	33	—
Pine, sugar	98	219
western white	62	148
Redwood, old-growth	86	210

[1]Based on weight when oven dry.

Source: U.S. Forest Products Laboratory, *Wood Handbook*.

first, followed by the bound water, and drying took place at an even rate, drying wood would present no problems. This, however, is not the case. The water present in the outer surface of the board, especially at the ends, evaporates very quickly. The free water in these areas is soon gone, followed by the bound water, long before any water has disappeared from the interior of the board (figure 4–8). This uneven drying leads to uneven shrinkage and results in surface checking, end checking, warping, and case hardening.

Drying wood is a slow and exacting process, whether by air or kiln. It is important to remember that even though wood may have been dried to 6% moisture content, the process is not permanent. There is no such thing as cured lumber. Curing implies a chemical process or permanent fix, which is, unfortunately,

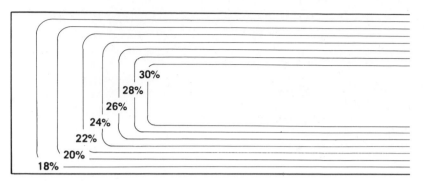

4—8. Average moisture content on the interior of a board dried four to six weeks.

impossible with wood. Atmospheric moisture can re-enter raw wood at any time.

EQUILIBRIUM MOISTURE CONTENT

A misconception commonly encountered is that wood breathes. It does not. As we know, heartwood is composed entirely of dead cells, while sapwood has some living cells located in the ray tissue. These die after the wood is cut. Nonetheless, wood is an organic substance that by its very nature still responds to climatic changes. Moisture is given off or absorbed as the seasons dictate. When the relative humidity rises, the wood fibers absorb moisture that penetrates from the outside and the wood swells. As the humidity decreases, excess mois-

ture is given off by the fibers to be reabsorbed by the surrounding air. Wood is constantly trying to maintain a balance between its moisture content and that of the surrounding environment. This balance is called the *equilibrium moisture content* (EMC). Simply expressed, it is the amount of moisture present in wood at a given temperature and relative humidity over a period of time (figure 4—9).

A closer look at figure 4—9 shows that humidity is only one factor in determining EMC. Temperature must also be taken into account. For instance, at a given temperature, as the humidity rises, the EMC of the wood increases dramatically. This is to be expected. On the other hand, as the relative humidity remains constant and the temperature rises, the EMC of the wood goes *down*. Water in the cell walls is in liquid form. As the temperature goes up, the water becomes gaseous and escapes into the warmer air.

RELATIVE HUMIDITY

Relative humidity is expressed as a percentage of the amount of moisture that the air is capable of holding at a given temperature. Warm air can hold more water vapor than cold air. For instance, air at 86°F (30°C) and 100% RH can

4—9. MOISTURE CONTENT OF WOOD IN EQUILIBRIUM WITH TEMPERATURE AND RELATIVE HUMIDITY

Temperature dry-bulb, °F	Relative humidity, percent																			
	5	10	15	20	25	30	35	40	45	50	55	60	65	70	75	80	85	90	95	98
30	1.4	2.6	3.7	4.6	5.5	6.3	7.1	7.9	8.7	9.5	10.4	11.3	12.4	13.5	14.9	16.5	18.5	21.0	24.3	26.9
40	1.4	2.6	3.7	4.6	5.5	6.3	7.1	7.9	8.7	9.5	10.4	11.3	12.3	13.5	14.9	16.5	18.5	21.0	24.3	26.9
50	1.4	2.6	3.6	4.6	5.5	6.3	7.1	7.9	8.7	9.5	10.3	11.2	12.3	13.4	14.8	16.4	18.4	20.9	24.3	26.9
60	1.3	2.5	3.6	4.6	5.4	6.2	7.0	7.8	8.6	9.4	10.2	11.1	12.1	13.3	14.6	16.2	18.2	20.7	24.1	26.8
70	1.3	2.5	3.5	4.5	5.4	6.2	6.9	7.7	8.5	9.2	10.1	11.0	12.0	13.1	14.4	16.0	17.9	20.5	23.9	26.6
80	1.3	2.4	3.5	4.4	5.3	6.1	6.8	7.6	8.3	9.1	9.9	10.8	11.7	12.9	14.2	15.7	17.7	20.2	23.6	26.3
90	1.2	2.3	3.4	4.3	5.1	5.9	6.7	7.4	8.1	8.9	9.7	10.5	11.5	12.6	13.9	15.4	17.3	19.8	23.3	26.0
100	1.2	2.3	3.3	4.2	5.0	5.8	6.5	7.2	7.9	8.7	9.5	10.3	11.2	12.3	13.6	15.1	17.0	19.5	22.9	25.6
110	1.1	2.2	3.2	4.0	4.9	5.6	6.3	7.0	7.7	8.4	9.2	10.0	11.0	12.0	13.2	14.7	16.6	19.1	22.4	25.2
120	1.1	2.1	3.0	3.9	4.7	5.4	6.1	6.8	7.5	8.2	8.9	9.7	10.6	11.7	12.9	14.4	16.2	18.6	22.0	24.7
130	1.0	2.0	2.9	3.7	4.5	5.2	5.9	6.6	7.2	7.9	8.7	9.4	10.3	11.3	12.5	14.0	15.8	18.2	21.5	24.2
140	.9	1.9	2.8	3.6	4.3	5.0	5.7	6.3	7.0	7.7	8.4	9.1	10.0	11.0	12.1	13.6	15.3	17.7	21.0	23.7
150	.9	1.8	2.6	3.4	4.1	4.8	5.5	6.1	6.7	7.4	8.1	8.8	9.7	10.6	11.8	13.1	14.9	17.2	20.4	23.1
160	.8	1.6	2.4	3.2	3.9	4.6	5.2	5.8	6.4	7.1	7.8	8.5	9.3	10.3	11.4	12.7	14.4	16.7	19.9	22.5
170	.7	1.5	2.3	3.0	3.7	4.3	4.9	5.6	6.2	6.8	7.4	8.2	9.0	9.9	11.0	12.3	14.0	16.2	19.3	21.9
180	.7	1.4	2.1	2.8	3.5	4.1	4.7	5.3	5.9	6.5	7.1	7.8	8.6	9.5	10.5	11.8	13.5	15.7	18.7	21.3
190	.6	1.3	1.9	2.6	3.2	3.8	4.4	5.0	5.5	6.1	6.8	7.5	8.2	9.1	10.1	11.4	13.0	15.1	18.1	20.7
200	.5	1.1	1.7	2.4	3.0	3.5	4.1	4.6	5.2	5.8	6.4	7.1	7.8	8.7	9.7	10.9	12.5	14.6	17.5	20.0
210	.5	1.0	1.6	2.1	2.7	3.2	3.8	4.3	4.9	5.4	6.0	6.7	7.4	8.3	9.2	10.4	12.0	14.0	16.9	19.3

SOURCE: U.S. Forest Products Laboratory, *Wood Handbook.*

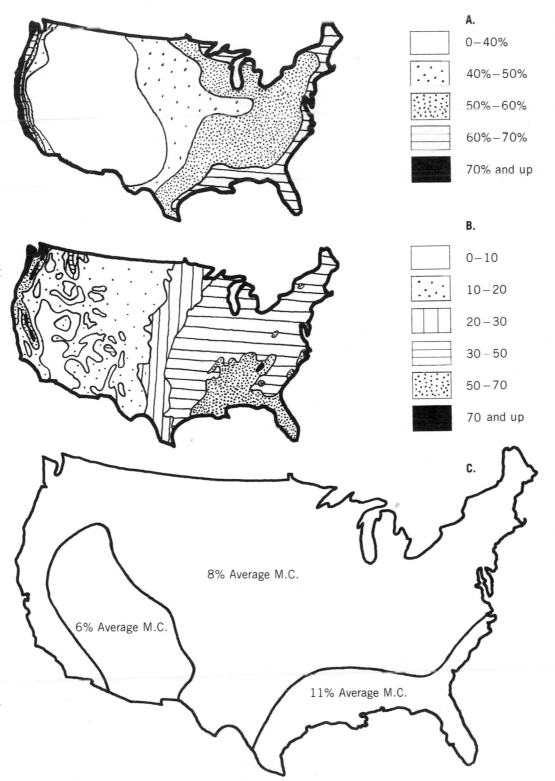

A.

	0–40%
	40%–50%
	50%–60%
	60%–70%
	70% and up

B.

	0–10
	10–20
	20–30
	30–50
	50–70
	70 and up

C.

8% Average M.C.

6% Average M.C.

11% Average M.C.

4–10. (A) Average relative humidity in July at noon, local time; (B) average annual precipitation in inches; (C) *average* recommended moisture content of wood for interior work. (C, by permission of Forest Products Laboratory, Madison, WI)

hold five times as much water vapor as air at 43°F (6°C) and 100% RH. Hence, it is a good idea for a well-equipped shop to have a thermometer and hygrometer or a wet and dry bulb thermometer to help indicate the relative humidity.

Location, as well as the time of the year, determines the average humidity. Figure 4–10 shows the average humidity in the United States for July, as well as the average rainfall. The third map takes both of these into account, as well as the corresponding equilibrium moisture content from figure 4−9, to arrive at a general composite map of average moisture content for wood intended for interior use in various parts of the country. This map should serve only as a rough guide, since local conditions can vary.

AIR DRYING

Numerous conditions influence the air drying of lumber, among them:

1. *Climatic conditions.* Generally speaking, very little drying of lumber is possible during the winter, particularly in those areas where the temperature remains below freezing. Surface moisture can evaporate by the process of sublimation, whereby the water goes from a solid state (ice) directly to a gaseous state (vapor) without becoming a liquid. Thus, only surface moisture evaporates. In those areas where winter temperatures are relatively mild, some drying will occur, so long as rainfall and humidity are not excessive. Drying rates are variable and depend on local weather conditions. The location of the drying pile and even its orientation to the sun and prevailing wind all influence the rate of evaporation.

2. *Species.* The wood type makes quite a difference when it comes to length of drying time. Specific gravity is a fairly good general indicator of drying rate. The lower the specific gravity, the faster the drying time. Therefore, the softwoods and the lighter species of hardwood dry faster under favorable conditions. The percentage of sapwood and heartwood also plays a part. For instance, sugar maple dries faster than northern red oak, even though they both have about the same specific gravity, because sugar maple has more sapwood. Figure 4−11 lists the approximate air drying times of native woods.

3. *Thickness.* The old rule of thumb, one year's drying for each inch of thickness, really has no basis in fact. First, it does not take species into account, and secondly, drying time is a function of the square of the thickness. This means that two-inch stock takes about four times as long to dry as one-inch stock. In fact, for some species the drying time is even longer than the square of the thickness. This is one reason (along with the differential between radial and tangential shrinkage, as is described in chapter 5) why it is next to impossible to dry entire logs without serious cracking or checking.

4−11. APPROXIMATE TIME TO AIR DRY GREEN 1-INCH LUMBER TO 20 PERCENT MOISTURE CONTENT

Species	Time
SOFTWOODS	Days
Bald cypress	100−300
Pine, eastern white	60−200
sugar	15−200
western white	15−150
Redwood	60−185
HARDWOODS	
Ash, white	60−200
Basswood, American	40−150
Beech, American	70−200
Birch, yellow	70−200
Butternut	60−200
Cherry, black	70−200
Elm, American	50−150
Hickory	60−200
Maple, sugar	50−200
Oak, northern red	70−200
northern white	80−250
southern red	100−300
southern white (chestnut)	120−320
Sweetgum, heartwood	70−300
sapwood	60−200
Sycamore, American	30−150
Walnut, black	70−200
Yellow-poplar	40−150

SOURCE: Raymond C. Reitz, *Air Drying of Lumber: A Guide to Industry Practice.*

4. *Grain pattern.* Quartersawn wood is slower to dry than plainsawn wood. The rays aid in drying, and although they are more prominent on quartersawn boards, not nearly so many of them are exposed on the face of the board.

5. *Pile construction and foundation.* The actual method of stacking the wood has a lot to do with the drying rate. The more space left between boards, the faster they dry. Many smaller piles dry faster than one large pile. The pile foundation should be well off the ground to allow for free air movement underneath. Weeds and debris should not obstruct the air flow. Finally, the ground surface must be well drained, with no standing water at any time.

PREPARATION OF THE WOOD

Proper preparation for drying wood can yield much higher returns in sound wood and in some cases can prevent total loss caused by checking and warping. Whenever possible, the pith of the tree should be cut out and discarded, as boards containing pith will invariably check. Larger planks or timbers will check, no matter how carefully they are dried (figure 4—12). Any heavy timbers or carving blocks must have the pith removed, if they are expected to dry without checking.

Since exposed pores or tracheids on the end grain surfaces promote too-rapid drying and result in checks (figure 4—13), it is wise to coat the ends of all wood to prevent any moisture loss from the end grain. Almost any impervious material will do. Wet wood can receive a primer of acrylic latex paint first. Aluminum paint, old oil paint, even melted paraffin will seal the wood. Coat ends almost immediately after sawing to minimize end checks; in woods like beech, checking will begin in a matter of hours. Oak is also quite susceptible (figure 4—14). Once checking develops, the damage (small cracks) will remain, even if closed later.

STACKING THE PILE

When constructing the lumber pile, it is important to keep the previous factors in mind. First, select a cleared, relatively flat, and well-drained site. Construct a foundation of cinder blocks, bricks, fieldstones, or very heavy timbers. Timbers are also useful on top of the foundation to raise the pile farther off the ground and to help level the foundation. Foundation blocks, posts, or rows can be between 18 and 36 inches (45—90 cm) apart and a minimum of 12 inches (30 cm) high, with 18—24 inches (45—60 cm) preferred. Figure 4—15 shows the proper construction of a pile of lumber for air drying. The width of the pile may vary, although 3—4 feet (.9—1.2 m) is ideal. Piles much narrower become tipsy; piles wider than 4 feet not only become hard to stack, but begin to retard air circulation and should have a space or flue left in the center for additional circulation. As long as the pile is stable, there is no restriction on height. In mill yards they are often stacked (with a forklift) to 35 feet (10.7 m).

Place the first layer of boards about one inch (2.5 cm) apart, with the ends of the boards even with the ends of the pile. Several shorter boards can be staggered to fill a row. Lay strips or stickers at right angles across the boards directly above the foundation planks, again 18—24 inches (45—90 cm) apart. The stickers must be of equal size to provide equal support between the layers. They also must be dry to prevent sticker staining. Add layers until the

4—12. Kiln-dried cherry plank with pith and stress check.

4—13. End checking in beech.

4—14. Surface checking in oak.

desired height is reached, all stickers stacked in line above the foundation supports. Several heavy planks or cinder blocks can be placed on top for extra weight to prevent warping. Finally, place corrugated metal, fiberglass, or plywood on top as a cover. Overhang is desirable on all sides for shade.

Air drying is not without risk, since the weather cannot be controlled. If drying takes place too rapidly, especially in full sun, surface checking will occur. On the other hand, if drying is too slow, mildew and fungal staining will

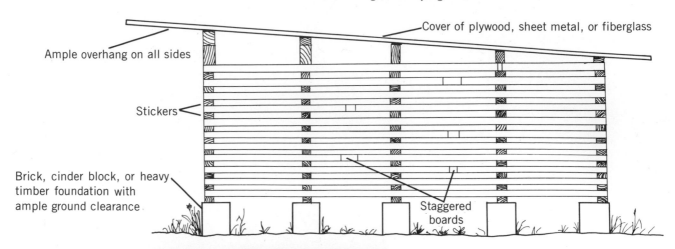

Cover of plywood, sheet metal, or fiberglass

Ample overhang on all sides

Stickers

Brick, cinder block, or heavy timber foundation with ample ground clearance

Staggered boards

4—15 (above). Properly stacked pile for air drying.

4—16 (right). Stacked pile with painted ends and cover.

4—17. Shed with wood drying in sawn order.

result. Following the rules closely will increase the chances of success: high, well-ventilated foundation; dry stickers; proper spacing of boards; sealed end grain; and a weighted cover with good overhang (figure 4—16).

Woodworkers who dry wood regularly sometimes prefer to build drying sheds. A very simple shed consisting of four posts and a roof takes little in time and material to construct. A lean-to behind a barn or shop also serves the purpose. Conceivably, an ideal drying shed would be oriented toward the prevailing wind, with huge doors at either end. These would remain open during good drying conditions and closed during inclement weather and in the winter.

Figure 4—17 shows a lean-to with a few piles of wood stacked and ready for end coating. The wood is kept in the order it was sawn. This makes it easier to select wood of the same color (from the same tree) and also facilitates book-matching.

During very dry periods, it is recommended that drying be slowed down somewhat early in the drying cycle to ease stresses in the wood. This can be done by covering the entire stack with a sheet of plastic. Moisture escaping from the wood will be trapped temporarily, slowing the surface shrinkage and subsequent checking. At the first signs of moisture condensation on the plastic, or the formation of mold, remove the plastic.

Under the best of conditions, outdoor air drying will yield an equilibrium moisture content of only 15%—20% in the wood. At this point the wood should be moved indoors to an area of artificial heat for further drying: a loft in the shop, a warm attic or basement, anyplace where artificial heat is present. A look back at figure 4—9 will enable review of the necessary temperature and humidity levels for wood to reach desired equilibrium moisture content.

Ideally, this last drying step to reach the intended indoor EMC should utilize an existing space and heat source, to avoid any additional costs. The biggest advantage to air drying is its low cost, since there is no need for fancy equipment. Anyone can air dry wood with most of the energy supplied by the sun and wind.

CALCULATING MOISTURE CONTENT

The woodworker must always be aware of the moisture content of his material, especially during the drying process. Careful monitoring of the rate of drying will determine when the wood reaches the equilibrium moisture content for a given location and climate. The wood can then be moved to an area of lower moisture content and/or higher temperature so that the moisture content can be further reduced. Then, when the wood has reached the desired level of moisture, it will be ready to use.

Several methods can be used to determine moisture content. A rough yet simple procedure for tracing M.C. (by way of the EMC) is by weight. A few pieces of wood are designated as samples, are weighed and recorded when green, and then are weighed again every few weeks thereafter. (Samples are recommended no matter what method is being used.) Weighing can be done, depending on the size of the sample, on a bathroom, baby, or food scale. Give the samples the same drying treatment as the rest of the wood. Record weights on a graph to give a visual representation of the moisture loss and the approximate point at which the wood will reach its EMC with its surroundings. At that point the sample will not longer lose weight under the present conditions. Figure 4−18 charts the weight loss for a large ash board. Increases as the wood dries are caused by periods of high atmospheric moisture.

If the prevailing temperature and humidity are known, a glance at a chart such as that in figure 4−9 will give a rough idea of the moisture content. For example, if the weight has remained more or less constant for the previous 8−10 weeks, the temperature has been averaging about 60°F (16°C), and the humidity, about 80%, then the moisture content would be in the neighborhood of 16%.

A more precise method of moisture detection involves the use of an accurate scale and an oven. A laboratory oven, kitchen oven, or even a toaster oven with accurate temperature control will work. Cut and weigh a sample small enough to fit into the oven. Place the sample in the oven at 212°−220°F (100°−104°C), and remove every hour for reweighing until no

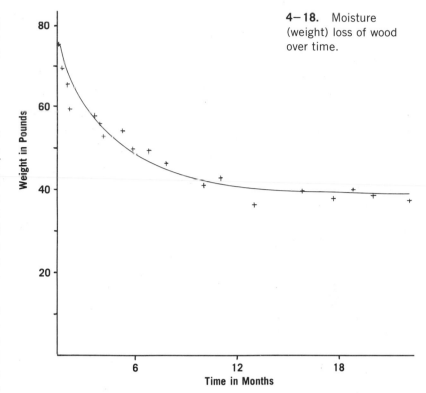

4−18. Moisture (weight) loss of wood over time.

more weight is lost. At that point, all the water will have been driven off and the moisture content reduced to 0% (oven dried). One can determine the moisture content of the sample before baking with the following formula:

$$M.C. = \frac{\text{Initial weight} - \text{Ovendry weight}}{\text{Ovendry weight}} \times 100$$

Other samples can be baked at any time, their weights used in the formula to determine their current M.C.

Weight and moisture content are directly proportional. The wood itself never changes weight; it merely takes on or releases moisture, which accounts for the weight change. This relationship allows the use of a graph for determining the approximate M.C. of identical samples (the samples should be from the same board, same size and weight). To do this, bake the first sample and record both its initial and ovendry weights such as the one shown in figure 4−19. Draw a straight line between the two points. If, for example, the initial weight of the samples is 48 ounces (1.36 kg), and at a later date the weight of a partially dry sample is found to be 40 ounces (1.13 kg), then the current moisture content of the sample can be figured as 52%.

Perhaps the easiest method of getting a direct reading of moisture is with an electric

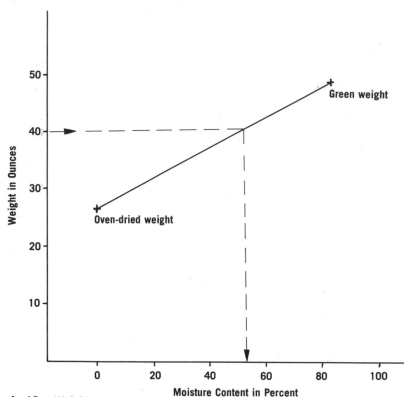

4—19. Weight to moisture content relationship.

Using these instruments is fairly simple. Drive the electrodes into the wood in such a manner that the current flows parallel to the grain. Now take the reading (figure 4—20). Usually a chart is included that allows for the different electrical properties of various species, as well as the temperature of the wood. Several readings should be taken at various points and averaged for greatest accuracy. Moisture meters are good to use not only when the wood is being dried, but also when construction of a piece of furniture begins. This gives an indication of the amount of expansion and contraction to be expected in backs, doors, drawers, and panels (see chapter 5). Any woodworker serious about drying a supply of wood should have a moisture meter available.

KILNS

Kilns are merely enclosures with varying degrees of atmospheric control. The difference between a kiln and a drying shed is that a kiln has a heat source for driving moisture from the wood. Heat can be produced by the sun, gas, oil, or electricity.

meter. Two types are most commonly available. The first, dielectric meters, generate a radio frequency that penetrates to a predetermined depth when placed against the wood. The power loss is translated and read as a moisture content percentage on the scale. The second type of meter measures the resistance of the wood to an electric current. Since water is a good conductor of electricity, the resistance to the passage of electricity is a function of moisture present in the wood. Thus, damp wood will offer a better path for the current and give a higher reading, whereas drier wood will offer more resistance and yield a lower reading. A deflecting needle shows the percentage of moisture content.

Solar Kilns   Solar kilns present a relatively new method of drying wood. Once the building is constructed, the energy required to drive moisture from wood is free. For small and medium wood operations, solar kilns offer a slower yet much cheaper wood-drying alternative, compared to commercial kilns. The only extra power needed is for driving fans to circulate air and control venting.

Solar kiln design possibilities are endless; a solar kiln can be built to handle loads of up to several thousand board feet. Figure 4—21 shows a plan for a simple solar kiln. Most kilns have large, angled, black collector plates under glass. The collector surface area should be roughly .1 ft² (90 cm²) for every board foot of intended drying capacity of the kiln. Hot air from the top of the collectors is circulated by fans and baffles through the stacked wood. The fans can be regulated by a thermostat to switch on when the temperature reaches about 80°F (27°C). Vents in the kiln can be controlled by motors and a humidistat, which can be preset and changed during the drying cycle. In this way the operator has direct control over the humidity level in the kiln, and surface checking can be all but eliminated. Kiln temperatures can reach 90°F (32°C) in the winter and up to 160°F (71°C) during summer operation.

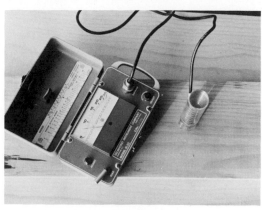

4—20.   Moisture meter in use.

Actual drying time varies, of course, according to species of wood, thickness, kiln construction method, amount of sunlight, location (latitude) of the kiln, and time of year. Depending on the above variables, 4/4 lumber can be dried in 12 to 50 days in the summer and in about 200 days over the winter. The result is wood with less checking, dried faster than air drying, with a moisture content down to 8%–10%.

Information on solar kilns can be obtained from the Forest Products Laboratory, Box 5130, Madison, WI 53705, as well as state forest experiment stations and extension agencies.

Commercial Kilns Commercial kilns are usually very large buildings that use energy to create heat and steam in order to dry wood in a very short time. Utilizing different kiln schedules (a series of temperature and humidity settings over a period of time) for different species and thicknesses, one can dry wood in a minimum amount of time with a minimum amount of checking, warping, and case hardening. Ordinary kilns operate at temperatures between 110°F (43°C) and 180°F (82°C); elevated-temperature kilns, between 180°F (82°C) and 212°F (100°C); and high-temperature kilns, above 212°F (100°C). Dehumidification kilns rely on the principle of removing moisture from the air (thus removing it from the wood) as opposed to extreme heat. By means of a compression unit, the moist air is condensed and the water is drained off.

Most elevated-temperature kilns are too large and expensive for small operations. Small dehumidification kilns can be purchased for

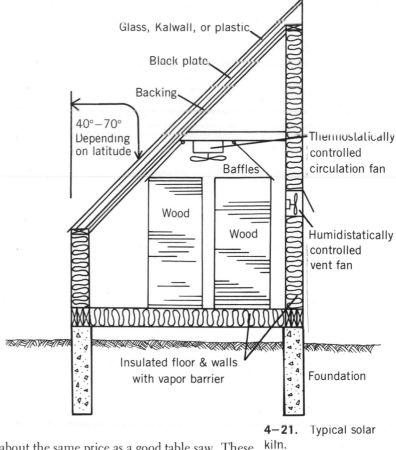

4–21. Typical solar kiln.

about the same price as a good table saw. These units are designed for kiln chambers drying as little as 600 board feet of lumber.

If the woodworker does not have the time, space, or inclination to air or solar dry wood, a commercial kiln is the practical alternative. Many mills and lumberyards have kilns and will dry small orders of wood if time, space, and kiln schedules permit.

CHAPTER 5

WORKING WITH SOLID WOOD

After all the work of harvesting, sawing, and drying the wood supply, it is easy to believe that the worst is over. At this point, however, the woodworker finds that the challenges are only beginning. How best to glue up panels? Which direction to orient the growth rings? How to remove warp and other imperfections in the wood? How to deal with moisture changes and wood movement, how to avoid the possibility of cracking?

During the summer months, drawers stick and doors swell shut. During the winter, when the already dry air is artificially heated, the relative humidity drops to 20, 10, and 5 percent, and gaps appear around doors, chairs loosen up, and solid furniture not designed to withstand the dryness cracks. Extreme changes in the humidity are the biggest problem confronting the woodworker.

But, although outside humidity changes may be quite abrupt, there is a time lag between changes in the air's moisture content and changes in the wood's moisture. One day of high or low humidity will not set the wood moving back and forth. It takes awhile for the moisture to penetrate into buildings, especially a tightly sealed, insulated one. A few more days are needed for the moisture to seep through a wood's finish or into the insides of drawers and case pieces. So, unless there is a prolonged wet or dry spell, the equilibrium moisture content of wood forever tries to catch up to the constantly changing weather patterns.

WOOD SHRINKAGE AND EXPANSION

Wood shrinking and swelling, or movement, results from changes in moisture content. As stated previously, wood does not start to shrink until all the free water in the cell cavities has evaporated. This is the *fiber saturation point*, at about 30% moisture content. Not until the bound water in the cell walls starts to evaporate does the cell wall, and consequently the entire piece of wood, start to shrink. This shrinkage varies from a low of just under 7% in volume for western red cedar and redwood to almost 20% in shellbark hickory and persimmon. Figure 5−1 shows the shrinkage values for native woods, from green to oven dried. This is the *total* first-time shrinkage from about 30% M.C. to 0% M.C. (ovendry).

Besides the volumetric shrinkage, the radial and tangential shrinkage is also listed. Tangential shrinkage is roughly twice that in the radial direction, because the wood rays run from the center of the tree to the outside, and anchor the wood fibers, which in turn inhibits shrinkage in the radial direction (figure 5−2). Since the wood cells tend to shrink equally around their girth but are restrained by the rays, a certain amount of stress causes weaknesses in radial planes. That is why some woods, especially those with large rays such as oaks, tend to check or honeycomb parallel to the rays.

What happens when a hole is drilled into

the face grain of a green board? Does the hole get larger or smaller as the wood shrinks? Most people think that as the wood around a hole shrinks, the hole must get bigger, like a doughnut. But while doughnut holes do get larger, holes in wood do not. Since wood shrinks across the grain when drying, the board gets narrower, and the hole, too, becomes narrower. Thus, a vertical oval will remain (figures 5–3 and 5–4).

Specific gravity also influences shrinkage. The more mass a wood has (that is, the higher the ratio of cellulosic material to the amount of air or cell cavities), the more it is likely to shrink. A space occupied by more cells will shrink *more* than the same space occupied by fewer cells. Figure 5–1 shows that the denser hardwoods generally shrink more than the softwoods.

Extractives in the cell cavities have a direct bearing on the amount of shrinkage. Sapwood will often shrink more than heartwood. Since the cell structure is identical, the difference is in the extractives—resins, tannins, oils, gums, and starches—which block (or bulk) the cell cavities and restrict their shrinkage.

Finally, a word about longitudinal or board-length, shrinkage. Why does figure 5–1 make no mention of it? Longitudinal shrinkage is very small; it generally runs between 0.1% and 0.2%. For a board 100 inches long (254 cm), this comes to 1/10–1/5 inch (.25 to .5 cm) between a totally green board at 30% M.C. and one dried to 0% M.C. If the board has been properly dried and used indoors, the EMC should range from 5% to 15%, meaning only one-third of that shrinkage must be dealt with. For all practical purposes, longitudinal shrinkage can be ignored.

PREDICTING MOVEMENT

Knowing how much a certain species of wood will move over the course of the seasons is important to the woodworker. Familiarity with the climatic conditions to be encountered is a first step. Is the piece being built in Seattle, Washington, only to be shipped to Tucson, Arizona? The expected range of the relative humidity should be established. The equilibrium moisture content for that expected range can be derived from figure 4–9.

A working knowledge of the amount of wood movement to be expected comes from experience. Each species shrinks a different amount. Figure 5–1 lists the total shrinkage

5–1. SHRINKAGE VALUES OF DOMESTIC WOODS

Species	Shrinkage from green to ovendry moisture content[1]		
	Radial %	Tangential %	Volumetric %
HARDWOODS			
Ash, white	4.9	7.8	13.3
Basswood, American	6.6	9.3	15.8
Beech, American	5.5	11.9	17.2
Birch, yellow	7.3	9.5	16.8
Butternut	3.4	6.4	10.6
Cherry, black	3.7	7.1	11.5
Chestnut, American	3.4	6.7	11.6
Elm, American	4.2	7.2	14.6
Hickory, shagbark	7.0	10.5	16.7
shellbark	7.6	12.6	19.2
Holly, American	4.8	9.9	16.9
Locust, black	4.6	7.2	10.2
Maple, sugar	4.8	9.9	14.7
Oak, red			
black	4.4	11.1	15.1
laurel	4.0	9.9	19.0
northern red	4.0	8.6	13.7
pine	4.3	9.5	14.5
scarlet	4.4	10.8	14.7
southern red	4.7	11.3	16.1
water	4.4	9.8	16.1
willow	5.0	9.6	18.9
Oak, white			
bur	4.4	8.8	12.7
chestnut	5.3	10.8	16.4
live	6.6	9.5	14.7
overcup	5.3	12.7	16.0
post	5.4	9.8	16.2
swamp chestnut	5.2	10.8	16.4
white	5.6	10.5	16.3
Persimmon, common	7.9	11.2	19.1
Sassafras	4.0	6.2	10.3
Sweetgum	5.3	10.2	15.8
Sycamore, American	5.0	8.4	14.1
Walnut, black	5.5	7.8	12.8
Yellow-poplar	4.6	8.2	12.7
SOFTWOODS			
Bald cypress	3.8	6.2	10.5
Cedar, E. red cedar	3.1	4.7	7.8
N. white	2.2	4.9	7.2
Pine, E. white	2.1	6.1	8.2
sugar	2.9	5.6	7.9
Redwood, old growth	2.6	4.4	6.8
young growth	2.2	4.9	7.0

[1]Expressed as a percentage of the green dimension.

SOURCE: U.S. Forest Products Laboratory, *Wood Handbook*.

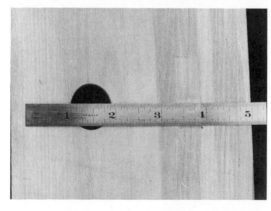

5-2. *Bottom*, green beech; *middle*, oven-dried quartersawn beech, showing radial shrinkage; *top*, oven-dried plainsawn beech, showing shrinkage in tangential direction.

5-3. A 1-inch hole (2.5cm) drilled in green beech.

5-4. The same board oven dried to 0% M.C. The hole is now only 29/32 wide (2.3cm) but still 1 inch (2.5cm) high.

$$\Delta D = \cfrac{D_1 (M_F - M_I)}{\cfrac{30(100) - 30 + M_I}{S_T}}$$

Where

ΔD = Change in dimension.

D_1 = Dimension (in inches or other units) at start of change.

M_F = Final moisture content (at end of change) in percent.

M_I = Initial moisture content (at start of change) in percent.

S_T = Tangential shrinkage (percent) from green to ovendry (figure 5-1). Use radial shrinkage if wood is quartersawn.[1]

Neither M_I nor M_F can be more than 30%, the fiber saturation point, when shrinkage starts.

This formula gives only an approximation of the actual shrinkage. Note that it does not take into account any sealing of the wood as a result of the finishes applied.

A minor point is the built-in safety factor for this equation. It is based on the values given in figure 5-1: total shrinkage of green wood to the oven-dried condition (0% M.C.). Shrinkage is, however, by definition, the percentage of change from the *green* condition. Swelling is based on the percentage of change from the *oven-dried* dimension. These are two different reference points. Also, the initial shrinkage from green wood is an irreversible change. All further dimensional changes are actually *smaller* than those that occur during the first drying. Wood is not a 100 percent elastic material, so that with each shrinkage and swelling cycle, the total movement becomes a minute amount less. This effect is known as *hysteresis*. Wood never stops moving, but the movement diminishes over the centuries. Consequently, the amount of overall movement is less than that indicated by the equation.

values of domestic woods, from the green to the oven-dried state for the radial and tangential directions.

For example, a plainsawn black cherry board 10 inches (25.4 cm) wide will move about 13/64 inch (.5 cm) between 14% and 6% moisture content. This is the indoor moisture range to which most wood is subjected. A quartersawn cherry board of the same width will move only about 7/64 inch (.25 cm) over the same moisture range.

The following equation is for those desiring a more thorough, scientific formulation of wood shrinkage:

CROSS-GRAIN GLUING

One of the biggest problems in cabinetry should now be apparent: how to build a piece of structually sound and stable furniture with a material that moves a significant amount in one direction (radially), twice that amount in another direction (tangentially), and an almost im-

---

[1]U.S. Forest Products Laboratory, *Wood Handbook*, pp. 14.

measurable amount in a third direction (lon
gitudinally)? The first and most important rule
of working with solid wood is to *never glue cross
grain*. That is, do not glue a strip, molding,
board, or plank perpendicular to a side, top,
bottom, or divider (figure 5–5). The reason
should be obvious. Wood does not change size
in length, only in width; therefore, attempting
to glue a piece at 90° across the grain will not
allow the second piece to expand and contract.
Something has to give, and the piece (whether
it is a chest side or tabletop) will crack. Figure
5–6 illustrates this result. Width is a prime
consideration here. Usually 1 or 2 inches (2.5
to 5 cm) of crossed grain are of little consequence, as in a mortise and tenon joint. The
previous rule is not being contradicted here;
most glues are not perfectly rigid and have a
small amount of "give," but only over a very
short distance. Two to three inches (5 to 7.5
cm) can even work under certain circumstances
(if the EMC stays relatively constant, and if a
good finish is used). Anything over 5 inches
(12.5 cm) is an open invitation to checking and
splitting. Whenever two or more boards are
glued *the grains must run in the same direction
or plane*. If they do not, then allowances must
be made to enable one of those boards to
change size across the grain with the seasons.
For some reason, this elementary yet very important principle is seldom discussed in high
school wood shops or beginning woodworking
texts.

GLUES AND GLUING

Correct gluing technique and the correct
choice of glue is essential to building stable furniture. Most small shops working with solid
wood are limited to several commercially available glues. These have a fairly long shelf life,
work well under general circumstances, do not
require elaborate drying equipment, and can be
purchased in small quantities.

The old standby is hide glue, manufactured from hoofs, tendons, and hides left over
from slaughter houses. Today's animal glues
are available premixed, with no heating necessary. Anyone who has ever worked with the
mix-your-own-and-heat-it-up animal or fish
glue will not mourn its passing into oblivion!
Franklin, Sears, and LePage are a few of the
most popular brands. Animal glue is about the
color and consistency of honey. It has a rela-

5–5. Cross-grain
gluing. The corner cleat
must not be glued since
the grain runs
perpendicular to the
adjacent sides.

tively long assembly time and requires several
hours of clamping time. Its lack of water resistance is a drawback to some and a bonus to
others. A good soaking will dissolve it, making
it ideal for anything that may need to be disas-
sembled in the future. For antique restoration it
is ideal, since the original was most likely as
sembled with hide glue.

Polyvinyl resin glue is probably the most
widely used by woodworkers. Manufactured by
Borden (Elmer's), Sears (white glue), and
Franklin (Evertite), and available at any hard-
ware store, it has a long shelf life, dries at room
temperature, leaves a clear glue line, and has a
clamping time of only about one hour. Although it has a low heat and moisture resistance, it does create a very strong joint, yet still

5–6. The result of
cross-grain gluing. The
molding kept the side
from shrinking and
caused it to crack.

provides a small amount of "cold creep," or "give," after drying.

One of the newer glues available is the cream-colored aliphatic resin glue. Available to the woodworker from Borden (Carpenter's Wood Glue) and Franklin (Titebond), aliphatic resin glue is more viscous, more heat resistant, and stronger, by test results. Because it produces a bond stronger than the wood, it is endorsed by many state departments of education for use on lathe work. A good all-purpose adhesive for the small shop, its only apparent drawback is its limited assembly time. It should not be used to assemble a complicated set of joints. Its short clamp time, about thirty minutes, makes it ideal for those with a small number of clamps.

Plastic resin glue (Weldwood) is properly called ureaformaldehyde. It is a tan power that, when mixed with water, can be made as thick as desired. It leaves an almost invisible glue line and is cold-water resistant. As an all-purpose glue it meets most common requirements, except that it is relatively high priced. Above 120° (49°C) it is not heat resistant. While heat resistance is not usually a high priority, one should keep in mind that if furniture glued with this

substance is to be used near wood stoves, in unventilated attics and sunporches, or locked in a car for transport on a sunny day, the joints could fail.

Resorcinol-formaldehyde (Weldwood, Franklin, Borden) is a two-part glue consisting of a dark liquid resin and a tan powdered hardener. This is a very high strength adhesive with complete water and heat resistance, making it perfect for exterior and marine use. A double spread is recommended. It has a long working life, giving it a long assembly time for complex pieces. A minimum temperature of 70°F (21°C) is required for proper curing. Clamping times range from seven to twelve hours, depending on the temperature. Its only drawbacks are a dark glue line, very noticeable on light woods, and a relatively high price.

Epoxy adhesives are made by a host of manufacturers, to meet almost any requirements. These glues are two-part mixes where "one drop holds it all." For general woodworking, their price is prohibitive, and besides, they are messy; one would do well to reserve epoxies for bonding wood to metal, slate, tile, glass, and most plastics.

For veneer work and plastic laminates, contact cement is used. It works a little differently from most other adhesives in that both surfaces are first coated, then allowed to dry. When positioned and brought into contact with each other, they form an immediate bond. There is no time for repositioning; no second chance. This eliminates its use for all joint work. Although its strength per square inch is lower than the other adhesives, its advantage is its use on large surfaces where clamping is difficult or impossible.

Joint failure directly on a glue line is always caused by poor gluing technique (including use of old glue) rather than the strength of modern glues. If properly applied and fit, no glue joint should ever break on the glue line. A good joint should be freshly machined or planed, well fitted, and free of dust, grease, oil, or wood shavings. The wood itself should be at 15% moisture content or below. Test clamp the joint for fit *before* gluing. Then, if the room and wood temperature is correct, and the glue has not passed its shelf life, both surfaces should be coated and clamped. Recommended clamping times for the existing temperature must be followed. Excess glue should be removed when partially dry, especially in corners. A cloth and chisel or scraper work best, since any smudges

5–7. Alternating growth rings result in a wavy top, while boards glued with the rings running in the same direction form one gentle cup, easier to hold down with fewer screws.

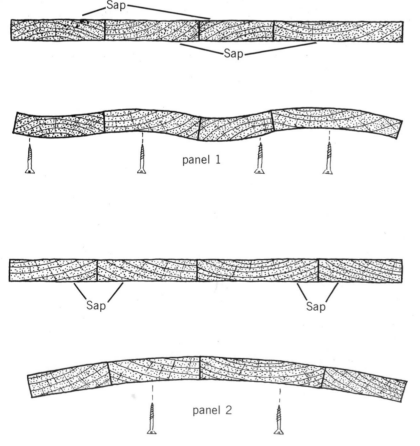

of glue will reappear after the finish is applied.

Glues hold by adhesion between the wood and the glue, which penetrates into the wood. The actual bond hardens either by the evaporation of a solvent, which links the molecules closer together, or by chemical reaction, which forms a stronger molecular complex.

Not all woods glue the same; some woods are more difficult to glue than others. All softwoods and most hardwoods have properties that allow them to be glued satisfactorily under most conditions. A small group of hardwoods needs special attention and should be glued only under optimum circumstances. These include *beech, hickory, Osage orange, persimmon, sugar maple,* and *yellow birch.* All relatively dense woods, they require a glue of high quality.

Gluing end grain to end grain is practically worthless with water-based glues. The joint will have only about 25 percent of the normal strength. A good scarf joint, with a slope of at least ten times the thickness of the wood, should be used. This procedure is seldom necessary in cabinet work, since wood is available in lengths up to 16 feet (4.9 m).

COMPENSATING FOR MOVEMENT

Gluing Panels

The days of single-plank tabletops are gone forever. And so, after a piece has passed the planning stage, panels must be glued up. A panel is nothing more than a series of boards of the correct length glued together edgewise to give the correct width. Stock should be cut to the required length, with enough boards to make up the width, allowing enough for jointing. Grain and color should be matched to give the appearance of continuous grain across the entire surface (see section on grain matching, p. 120). When gluing panels one must choose which side of the board faces up. If all boards are quartersawn, this presents no problem—either side will do. As noted previously, however, plainsawn lumber (with its wide, wavy pattern) has a tendency to warp; all conditions being equal, the growth rings have a tendency to cup away from the center of the tree. Therefore, most texts will recommend that the growth rings be alternated; one board up, one board down. Then, as the individual boards in the panel cup, the worst that can result is a wavy panel. Gluing together all boards with the rings running in the *same* direction will result in an

eventual cup much more pronounced than the small waves of the previous method. But, assuming that both panels will be used as tabletops, the more pertinent question may well be: which panel is easier to keep *flat*? To keep the small waves in panel 1 flat, almost every board in that panel would have to be screwed down; whereas only one or two screws would be sufficient to hold down Panel 2 (figure 5—7). What is more important is that by placing all growth rings in the same direction, with the older wood (that which grows toward the center of the tree) *up*, any sapwood can be left on the board and be put under the table. This saves quite a bit of wood, especially in cherry and walnut or wherever the appearance of sapwood is not desirable.

Jointing boards is a quick process with a power jointer or, after a little practice, with a long hand plane. A crisp, clean butt joint is all that is necessary for optimum strength in panels. Fancy tongue and groove joints are used in industry so that boards can be aligned by machine, but add no more to the strength of the joint. Doweled joints are not worth the effort either; again, they help to align the members but add little, if anything, in strength. Moreover, since the dowels are inserted at right angles to the boards, this can result in cross-grain gluing if glue finds its way into the holes, and can actually lead to cracking along that joint. The hole itself has only two small areas of long-face grain, the rest being end grain and contributing to a weak joint. This explains why dowels are not advisable in tables or chairs as replacements for mortise and tenon joints, which are much stronger.

Some texts also recommend leaving a $1/64$-inch (.35-cm) gap at the center of two boards about to be glued, but this technique is recommended only when the boards are expected to shrink further. The assumption here is that clamps will close the gap until the glue dries (which they do), and then as the boards dry the ends will shrink across the grain, relieving the pressure at the center. As noted previously, moisture exchange between wood and air occurs most rapidly at the ends of the boards. So the ends will reach EMC much faster than the center sections. Now suppose that the panel is glued up in a heated shop in the middle of winter, when no further possible shrinkage is likely to occur. The center of the boards, under pressure when clamped, is likely to undergo additional pressure as the ends of the boards take up moisture and expand; this can lead to splits near those glue joints. The moral here is to use the moisture meter in the center *and* the ends of the boards (especially after a long or severe humidity change) before leaving any kind of a gap. Anticipation of future humidity conditions can go a long way in preventing checks and splits.

GRAIN DIRECTION IN CASES

Bureaus, kitchen cabinets, cupboards, desks, stereo cabinets, dressers, blanket boxes, and display cases are all considered "case goods." Whether any of the six sides are open is not important. The outer box, without its various drawers or doors, is called the carcass. From the cabinetmaker's point of view, one of the primary considerations in constructing the carcass is which way to run the grain around it. By maximizing the amount of grain running in one direction or plane, cross-grain construction is minimized. That leaves only two or three choices, as figure 5−8 indicates. The most common method in case construction is to have the grain run up one side, across the top to the other side, and down to the bottom (A). With this method the carcass expands from the front

to the back, while its height and width remain constant. This front-to-back movement ensures that the size of the front remains the same, making drawers and doors easier to fit. The second method (B) is usually most suitable in blanket box construction. Here the grain runs around the left side, front, right side, and back, like a belt. This means the top and bottom remain the same size, but the box itself gets taller or shorter as the seasons change. That creates no problems, since there are no doors or drawers to fit. The lid, however, is another matter, since it shrinks and expands in width, especially as it is usually hinged in the back; all the movement will therefore be most apparent in the front. The third option is to have the grain run front to back on both sides and the top, which aesthetically and structurally is the most unsatisfactory (C).

CASE CONSTRUCTION

Once the grain direction has been decided and the panels glued, the actual building process can begin. Sand both sides and the top, joint one edge, and cut to width. Cut sides, perfectly square, to height, and the top to length. Select the best sides of all three panels and mark as the outsides. Next, rabbet or groove the back edges to accept the back. Depending on the type of joint used on the top and whether or not a molding is to be used, the rabbet in the top may have to be stopped. Now cut the joint used to fit the top to the two sides. This could be a screwed butt joint, a single or double rabbet joint, dovetails, or a splined miter. A little planning is in order for the next step, since it is now time to make the dadoes and grooves for any interior dividers, shelves, doors, or drawers; it is much easier to accomplish this *before* the pieces are glued. Now the top can be screwed, glued, or clamped to the sides. A temporary spacer will keep the bottom of the sides parallel. While the glue is drying, you can construct the bottom and any dividers. If solid shelves, dividers, and bottoms are used, this presents no problem, since they will slide into the dadoes and the grain will be in the same direction as the top and sides, assuring that all movement will be front to back. In some instances drawer dividers are merely frames that allow the drawer to slide in and out, yet save a considerable amount in weight and raw material (figure 5−9). These frames, however, will not move in the same manner a solid divider would, since the sides of the frames run at 90° to the grain of the case sides. Because of

5−8. Case grain direction options.

this potential movement, frames cannot be glued into place, but are best attached by nailing. The case is turned upside down, and the frames slid into the dadoes, starting at the top (which is the bottom dado, now that the case is upside down). Finishing nails are driven at a slight diagonal through the frame and into the case side. They must not show underneath the frame or on the outside of the case side. Two or three nails will suffice to hold the frame in place, yet will allow the sides to move. Nailing across the grain is allowable, since the nails permit movement of the wood. Figure 5−10 shows the basic steps in case assembly.

This process is continued until all frames are in place. The last one, the bottom, should be solid wood if it is to house an open compartment. If it is merely the last drawer frame, then it must be constructed with grooves and floating dust panels. If desired, all frames can have dust panels. (See section on panel and frame construction, p. 115.)

Squaring the case prior to attaching the back is most important. Place the carcass face down either on the floor or on sawhorses. Assuming that both sides were cut to the same length and the top and bottom of the case are the same width, a potentially square box exists. Measure from the top left corner to the bottom right, and from the top right corner to the bottom left. These measurements should be identical. If they are not, a clamp can be used to pull the longer of the two opposing corners into position. The carcass is now ready to accept the back.

In solid wood construction, backs are usually loosely fitted individual boards, rather than one solid glued-up panel. By using smaller individual pieces, the total shrinkage and expansion of the back will be distributed across the entire width, rather than at both sides of the back, as each board is allowed to move independently. One of three commonly used joints can be chosen to allow movement yet exclude dust and light from the case: spline, ship lap, or tongue and groove (figure 5−11). Under no circumstances should any of these joints be glued; they *must* remain loose in order for the back to move. The choice of joints is not totally arbitrary. If the back is to be made of expensive primary wood (if it is an open case or if glass doors are used), then a spline is called for, since up to ½ inch (1.25 cm) is lost in overlap on the tongue and groove and ship lap. If the back is to be thinner (on a small display case or desk),

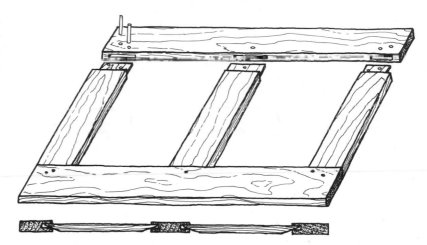

5−9. Drawer divider construction and cross section showing dust panels.

then a ship lap is less subject to breakage during assembly than either an extremely thin tongue or spline. Tongue and groove joints can be used on thicker backs.

In determining the amount of gap to leave between the individual boards, common sense and a moisture meter are both helpful. Kiln-dried wood used in the middle of January will expand in a few months, so leave a bigger gap. Wood at 14% M.C. used in July can usually be butted tightly. Again, the "movement" formula (page 106) can be used to predict the exact amount to plan for. Now nail the back across the top and all dividers, and down both sides with finishing nails. It is good practice to countersink the nails.

Turn the case over and recheck for squareness. It is now ready for face strips or a full front frame to cover the drawer dividers. The face strips are made of primary wood, dovetailed into both sides, and glued to the secondary wood dividers. No problems here, even though two different woods are glued, since the grains run in the same direction.

MOLDING

The case can now be sanded and is ready for any molding that needs to be applied. In applying molding, a difficult situation is encountered. A top molding must be flush to the surface, remain tight at the miter, remain the same width as the case, and be strong enough to serve as an occasional handle to lift and move the case. Obviously, a small piece of wood attached across the grain of a case cannot meet all these requirements at the same time. A look at almost any piece of antique case work will attest to that. All too often, glue is used in the vain hope of stopping the inevitable movement of the case side. Figure 5−6 shows the result.

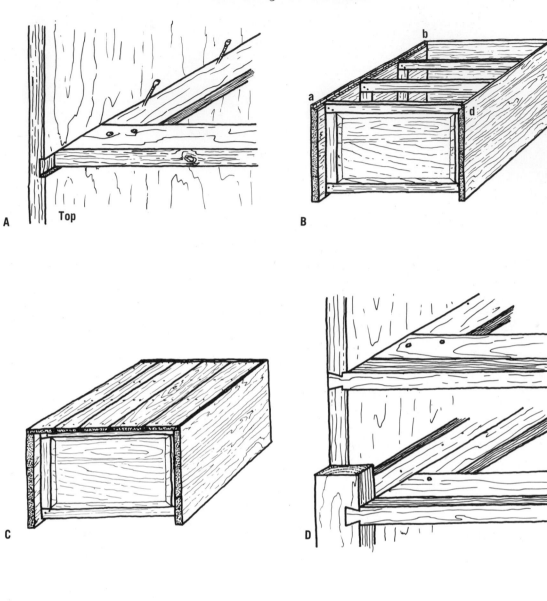

A Top

B

C

D

5–10. Case assembly procedure: (A) After top is attached to sides, turn case upside down, and nail drawer frames into place from below. (B) Square the case to adjust a—c to equal b—d. (C) Nail back into place. (D) Apply face frame, either a partial frame (top half) or full frame (bottom half). (E) Case is ready for sanding on all surfaces. (F) Apply moldings. Construct and fit doors and drawers.

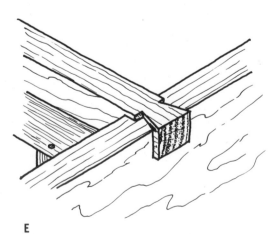

E

F

Molding on antique furniture was almost always applied with finishing nails. This served the purpose, but just barely: while the molding was held in place and the nails did allow movement, the mitered corner opened and closed at the whim of the weather, and eventually the molding worked itself loose. A slight improvement over this method is to glue the mitered joint and the first inch of molding, use finishing nails on the rest of the length, and then sink a screw as close to the miter as possible. This can be done from the inside, if there is room to work, or directly into the molding. A plug cut from the waste material of the miter can be used to fill the hole (figure 5—12). With this method a small amount of glue and a screw keep the miter closed year-round, the finishing nails allow for movement, and all the expansion and contraction of the case side is limited to the back—a compromise at best, but one that works well. The front molding can of course be glued its full length, since the top and any face frame are running side to side also.

Another alternative is not to add molding, but rather to shape a molding pattern directly into the front and two sides of the top (figure 5—13). The top must be wider and longer than the case to allow for the overhang and can be attached with screws and cleats. This works especially well on blanket box tops. Trying to apply molding to three sides of a single board top (or panel) is chancy at best; molding must be anchored along both sides (which are end grain), and neither nails, glue, nor screws can hold it. The "integrated molding" is much easier to construct, and movement ceases to be a problem.

CLEATS, RIBS, AND STABILIZERS

Cupping is the major problem of blanket box tops, slab doors, and other unsupported panels. Unless perfect quartersawn stock is used, some cupping and warping is inevitable. Heavy hardwood cleats or ribs are applied perpendicular to the grain to act as stabilizers. Clamping the ribs into place tests their strength in counteracting the cupping. If the ribs do not completely straighten any warp, a thicker rib can be used, or the rib can be set on its edge (assuming it is rectangular in cross section) to supply more strength. Two final alternatives are to use a bowed board as you cleat, or to shape the mirror image of the cup into the cleat. Ideally, the two will counteract each other.

In attaching the cleat to the panel, the po-

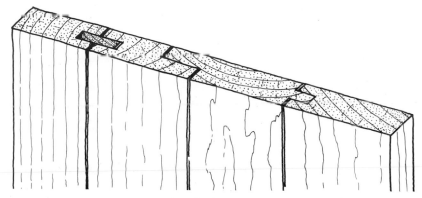

5—11 (above). Back jointing options (left to right): spline, ship lap, and tongue and groove.

5—12. Molding can be screwed and plugged at miter.

5—13. Molding shaped directly into top.

tential movement of the panel must be provided for. First, use an odd number of screws to attach the cleat to the panel. Drill the center screw straight into the cleat to anchor it firmly in the middle. That way only half the total movement must be contained on either side of the center. The remaining screw holes must be slotted to allow for movement. The slot should run in line with the anticipated movement: perpendicular to the panel grain, in line with the cleat. The farther a screw is from the center, the wider the slot should be (figure 5—14). To

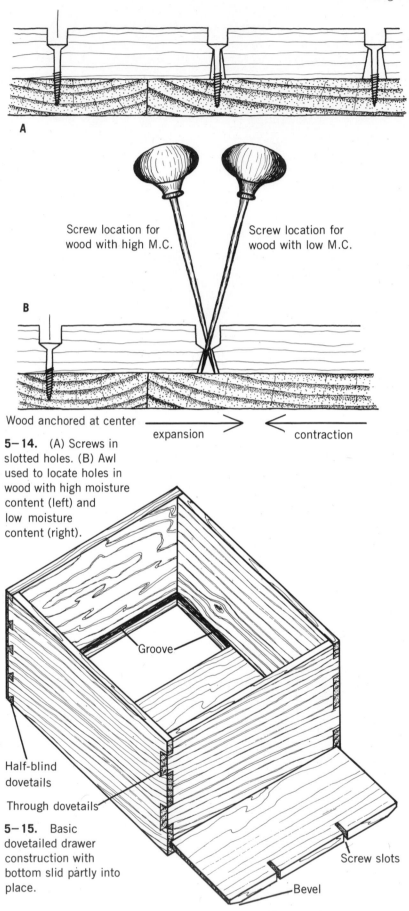

Screw location for wood with high M.C.

Screw location for wood with low M.C.

Wood anchored at center

expansion → ← contraction

5–14. (A) Screws in slotted holes. (B) Awl used to locate holes in wood with high moisture content (left) and low moisture content (right).

Groove

Half-blind dovetails

Through dovetails

5–15. Basic dovetailed drawer construction with bottom slid partly into place.

Bevel

Screw slots

locate the screw in the slot, poke a hole at either end of the slot with a scratch awl. When the cleat is removed the holes mark the location of the slots. Use a moisture meter to determine moisture content. If the panel is relatively dry and expansion is expected, drill the screw holes in the panel closer to the center screw. Conversely, if the panel has a high moisture content and shrinkage is expected, drill the holes closer to the outside edges. Common sense dictates anything in between.

An older method utilizes dovetailed stabilizer strips. Several flared dadoes are cut or routed into the panel, across the grain and about one-third to two-thirds of the thickness of the panel. Dovetail-shaped hardwood strips, with the grain running in the long direction, are cut to fit and forced into the dadoes. No glue is used, but a small brad can be driven in at the center. Although the result is better looking, it does not hold as well as a cleat.

DRAWERS

Drawer construction is quite straightforward (figure 5–15). Better-quality furniture usually incorporates dovetails. Dovetail joints can be cut by hand to suit *any* drawer size; size is not limited by the fit of router jig. Drawer openings should not change in size if the piece was planned correctly. The only movement to worry about is in the height of the drawer itself, which will increase or decrease depending on seasonal conditions. The gap above the drawer thus must be sized to suit anticipated movement in the future. Winter-built, dry wood drawers are loose; summer-built, moist wood drawers are tight. The exact gap size depends on the drawer height. Obviously an 8-inch (20 cm) drawer needs a bigger gap than a 3-inch (7.5 cm) drawer. Nine or 10 inches (23 or 25.4 cm) is about the maximum height for most drawers, except files. Anything higher becomes cumbersome and difficult to find things in. The gap, too, becomes too large to be aesthetically pleasing, unless lips are used on the drawers.

Drawers can be up to 24 inches (61 cm) deep, which results in at least ½ inch (1.25 cm) of movement in the bottom. Again, a look at antique furniture construction is helpful. To begin with, one should build the drawer about ½ inch (1.25 cm) shorter than the depth (front to back) of the opening. Run grooves to accept the drawer bottom into both sides and the front. Make the back to fit directly *above* the groove; the bottom can then be slid into place after the

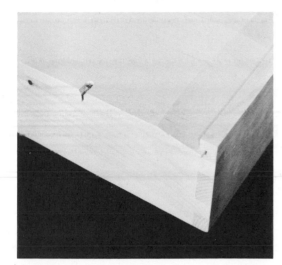

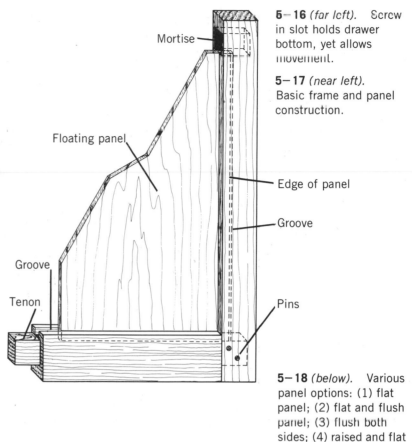

5–16 *(far left).* Screw in slot holds drawer bottom, yet allows movement.

5–17 *(near left).* Basic frame and panel construction.

Mortise

Floating panel

Edge of panel

Groove

Groove

Tenon

Pins

5–18 *(below).* Various panel options: (1) flat panel; (2) flat and flush panel; (3) flush both sides; (4) raised and flat panel; (5) raised both sides; (6) raised both sides, set in molded frame.

entire drawer is assembled. Run grain direction of the bottom side to side; that way, there is less bowing when weight to placed into the drawer and, as the bottom expands and contracts, it can move in and out the back. On small drawers the bottom can be attached with a brad through the bottom into the back. The best way to attach a bottom to a large drawer is to use a screw in a slot to keep the bottom from sagging (figure 5–16). The screw head supports the bottom while allowing it to move.

FRAME AND PANEL CONSTRUCTION

One of the oldest and most ingenious methods for reducing overall wood movement is frame and panel construction (figure 5–17). A good-sized slab panel will move up to ½ inch (1.25 cm), depending on its width. While a storm or shed door could accommodate a space that size and a ¾ inch (1.9 cm) door stop would keep out drafts, for furniture it would simply be too much. A frame consisting of 2½-inch or 3-inch (6.3 or 7.5 cm) stiles and rails will change less than ⅛ inch (3 mm) at the most, since only two 3-inch (7.5 cm) members move. Now, if a groove is cut inside that frame and the panel is allowed to float, it can move as it needs to without affecting the overall door size. This, then, is the theory behind frame and panel construction: a frame of any size, composed of relatively small members, is grooved to allow a large panel to float back and forth, with all apparent movement occurring inside the frame grooves. Dowels, because of their weakness, should not be used for the frame. A well-made door has mortise and tenon joints, pinned, at the intersections of all stiles and rails.

Panels to fit the frame can be made in a

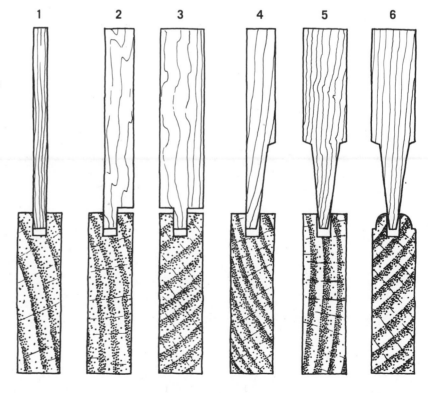

1   2   3   4   5   6

wide variety of styles and shapes. Figure 5–18 shows a few of the more common types. The first is simply a flat panel, the same thickness as the width of the groove. It is very easy to make and fit. Numbers 2 and 3 are variations, flat on both sides, yet 2 is two-thirds the thickness of the frame, rabbeted on one side only, while 3 is the same thickness as the frame, rabbeted on both sides and appearing flush on both sides. With both of these panels, care and judgment are needed in allowing adequate space between the rabbet shoulder and frame for panel expansion. Number 4 is a panel, raised on one side, again two-thirds the thickness of the frame, while 5 is raised on both sides. The last illustration is the same raised panel, this time set into a molded frame.

A few words of warning: grooves in the stiles must be deep enough to allow for future expansion. The wider the panel, the deeper the groove. Panels must be presanded *and* prefinished. Unless the panel is bone-dry, any shrinkage at a later date will reveal raw wood at both edges. No glue should be allowed on the panel, especially when assembling the frame. Panel fit should be snug, yet free floating in the groove. Loose panels are never glued; two small brads on the back side, through the rail edges at the centers, will hold them in place and still permit side-to-side movement. Paint on a completed door acts as glue, anchors the panel along all its edges, and often causes cracking. Doors to be painted should have a few coats of impervious paint applied to the panels prior to assembly, thus sealing the wood.

Frame and panel construction is not limited to doors. Dressers, bureaus, and other case pieces can also be built with this method. The stiles in this instance are the four corner posts or legs with grooves cut into two adjacent sides. Horizontal cross stretchers, also grooved, correspond to the rails. Most cases built in this fashion have one or more panels on each side and the back, with an open framed front to house doors or drawers. The top is attached with cleats and fitted last.

TABLES

Tables are good first pieces for beginning woodworkers, as well as a challenge for expert joiners and designers. Consisting only of one or more legs, a few rails or supports, and a large, flat surface, a table may, nonetheless, be made according to an endless list of variable possibilities. The top can be a single solid slab, several pieces with hinged leaves, or even a frame and flush panel.

Attaching the top to the base seems to present the most problems. Several options are available to allow a wide expanse of wood to move, yet remain firmly anchored to the base (figure 5–19). One method (A) is to drill directly through the table skirt and use flat-head screws of the correct length. Screws in the center of the two skirts running perpendicular to the grain of the top can be drilled straight. Screw holes on either side of the center must be "ovallized" to allow for movement of the top. The farther away form the center, the longer the oval (See "Cleats, Ribs, and Stabilizers, p. 113, and figure 5–14.)

An alternative with thin skirts is to screw a cleat along the top edge of the table skirt and to drill through the cleat (B). The same method of oval screw holes is used.

A technique often found on antique furniture, including tables, is to use pocket holes (C). A three-sided notch is chiseled into the inside of the skirt, near the top. The pocket resembles a corner of a pyramid. Holes are drilled through the pocket, ovallized as necessary, and the base is then screwed to the top.

The last method illustrated (D) uses grooves and wooden holding fingers. The grooves, on the top inside edges of the skirts, are best cut before the base is assembled. Fingers on the hold-downs must fit into the grooves but must not be slid all the way in if the top is expected to expand further. Since the hold-downs themselves slide in and out of the grooves, they can be screwed straight into the top, without oval holes.

These are not by any means the only methods used to secure tabletops. Other techniques range from sliding dovetails to commercial metal clips. Case pieces, which do not have their tops directly dovetailed, rabbeted, or mitered into the sides, can have their tops attached by any of these means, as well.

Bread-boarded ends (also called end clamps or end cleats) are the only other major problem of cross-grain construction in tables. Bread boards are merely cleats dovetailed or mortised and tenoned onto the ends of panels. They are used to help keep large panels relatively flat where there are a minimum number of stretchers, skirts, or supports under the panel. Although this treatment is appropriate to any straight-ended table with a large overhang, it is most often seen on the old trestle tables.

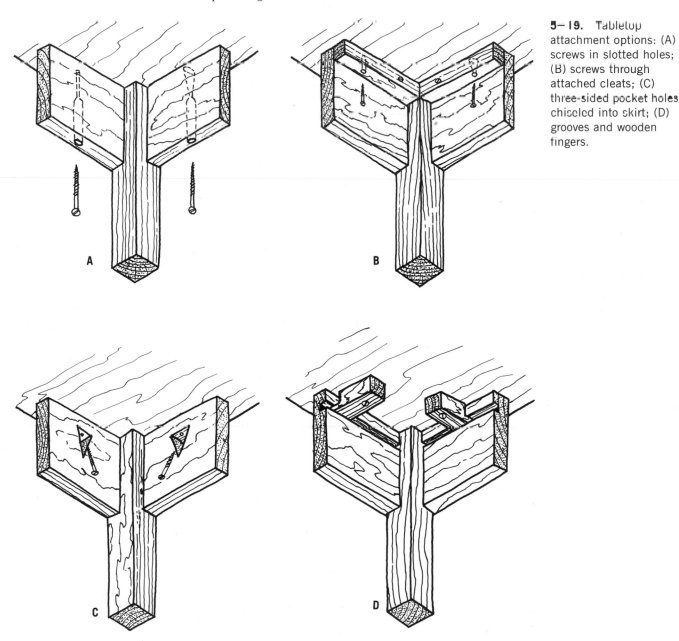

5-19. Tabletop attachment options: (A) screws in slotted holes; (B) screws through attached cleats; (C) three-sided pocket holes chiseled into skirt; (D) grooves and wooden fingers.

Over the years, two basic methods for attaching bread boards have proven to be most successful. The first, a full-length sliding dovetail, creates a handsome and functional joint. The pin of the dovetail is cut along both ends of the tabletop, directly into the end grain. An outline of that pin is transferred to the end grain of the bread board, and the dovetailed groove is cut along the length of one edge. Alternatively, grooves can be cut first and transferred to the table ends. Whichever method is chosen, the pin must slide into the groove. A snug fit is desirable, but not one so tight as to split the bread board. The joint line where the table end grain meets the board must be crisp, clean, and tight. A sloppy joint here will not serve the purpose. To keep the bread board in place, a single dowel, through the center, will lock it and allow it to move on either side.

An alternative method, which is a little less exacting, is to use a long mortise and tenon joint. A tenon one-half to one-third the thickness of the top is cut into both ends, the full length, and a minimum of 1 inch (2.5 cm) wide. Roughly ¾ inch (1.9 cm) is cut off both ends of the tenon. Bread boards are prepared next. They should be at least 1 inch wider than the tenon and several inches longer than the

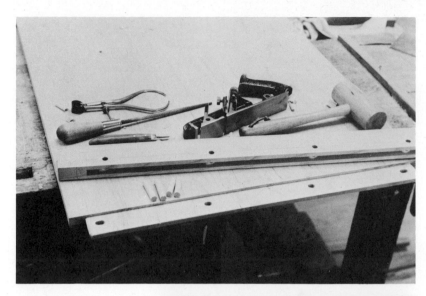

5–20 *(above)*. Bread board ready to be attached.

5–21. Bread board in winter; tabletop shrinks.

5–22. Bread board in summer; tabletop swells.

inch longer, depending on the overall width of the table.

To achieve a snug fit, use a rabbet plane and a caliper to detect and remove thick spots on the tenon. After both boards are fitted, long bar clamps or pairs of shorter ones fitted across the length of the table will hold the boards in place. Drill three to six holes (vertically through the center line of the tenon) through the bread boards. Remove clamps and boards and ovalize the holes in the tenons to permit movement within the groove. If an odd number of holes are drilled, keep the center hole round, while filing the holes farther from center into wider and wider ovals. If expansion of the top is anticipated, file holes toward the center. Conversely, if shrinkage is expected, file holes toward the outside edges. This permits the pins to remain stationary since the bread board does not change in length, yet allows the tenon to move back and forth. Figure 5–20 shows a tabletop with bread boards ready to be attached.

A top treated in this manner will be flush about twice a year. As it shrinks in the winter the bread boards will protrude slightly (figure 5–21). During the summer, the top itself will be wider (figure 5–22).

WORKING QUALITIES OF WOOD

A thorough knowledge of the working qualities of wood is essential to any phase of woodworking. Some woods machine better than others. Generally speaking, the softer a wood is, the more easily it yields to hand tools. The tools, however, must be sharp. White pine, for instance, is a marvelous wood to plane and chisel, yet with dull tools it simple tears. A knowledge of the wood's anatomy is also very helpful. Ordinarily, cherry planes very well, but occasionally, wavy grain will make hand planing almost impossible. Rock maple is one of the finest turning woods, yet the bird's eye or tiger stripe grain will consistently chip on the lathe. Shaping willow or aspen is next to impossible. Reaction wood, which is difficult to detect in a single board, becomes quite apparent when it is sanded. The surface is always fuzzy, more so in the softer woods. Figure 5–23 offers a listing of the major machining and related properties of most hardwoods. A full knowledge of how each wood reacts to various tools takes years to acquire.

Besides taking the machining qualities of a

table width, to facilitate removal when fitting. A stopped groove is cut into the edge of the board. The groove should be ¼ to ½ inch (.6 to 1.25 cm) *longer* than the tenon to allow for table width expansion. A moisture reading of the tabletop at this point is very helpful. For an extremely dry top, the groove may need to be ⅝ wood into consideration, decisions must also be made as to the correct wood for a specific purpose. Unfortunately, in today's mass marketplace, price and availability seem to be the major criteria. Chairs with pine legs, outdoor furniture of beech or birch, sugar pine exterior doors, and particle board bookshelves are all destined for disintegration. The old-timers often used four, five, or six different woods in one piece of furniture, each wood serving a specific function no other wood could match. A typical Windsor chair had its back and arms made of ash, beech, hickory, or oak, because those woods steamed and bent well. The spindles were made of ash for extra flex, while the seat was easily carved out of 2-inch white pine. Legs and stretchers were turned from rock maple for strength. Coopers used white oak for whiskey barrels since the tyloses in the pores sealed the wood. Red oak was used for grain and storage barrels, basswood for berry boxes. The Shakers made their oval boxes of elm, cherry, birch, or oak, some with white pine bottoms. These boxes had specific purposes; some were used for dry measure, others as sewing baskets. Even the fasteners on the fingers were carefully chosen copper, since regular tacks would rust or be attacked by the acid in oak.

No butcher would have a birch chopping block. Sycamore was the preferred wood, and it was used end-grain up for years of service. Cutting boards and wooden kitchenware were usually of maple or beech—never walnut, since it would impart a flavor of its own to the food

5–23. SOME MACHINING AND RELATED PROPERTIES OF SELECTED DOMESTIC HARDWOODS

Kind of wood	Planing— perfect pieces	Shaping— good to excellent pieces	Turning— fair to excellent pieces	Boring— good to excellent pieces	Mortising— fair to excellent pieces	Sanding— good to excellent pieces	Steam bending— unbroken pieces	Nail splitting —pieces free from complete splits	Screw splitting —pieces free from complete splits
	%	%	%	%	%	%	%	%	%
Alder, red	61	20	88	64	52	—	—	—	—
Ash	75	55	79	94	58	75	67	65	71
Aspen	26	7	65	78	60	—	—	—	—
Basswood	64	10	68	76	51	17	2	79	68
Beech	83	24	90	99	92	49	75	42	58
Birch	63	57	80	97	97	34	72	32	48
Birch, paper	47	22	—	—	—	—	—	—	—
Cherry, black	80	80	88	100	100	—	—	—	—
Chestnut	74	28	87	91	70	64	56	66	60
Cottonwood	21	3	70	70	52	19	44	82	78
Elm, soft	33	13	65	94	75	66	74	80	74
Hackberry	74	10	77	99	72	—	94	63	63
Hickory	76	20	84	100	98	80	76	35	63
Magnolia	65	27	79	71	32	37	85	73	76
Maple, bigleaf	52	56	80	100	80	—	—	—	—
Maple, hard	54	72	82	99	95	38	57	27	52
Maple, soft	41	25	76	80	34	37	59	58	61
Oak, red	91	28	84	99	95	81	86	66	78
Oak, white	87	35	85	95	99	83	91	69	74
Pecan	88	40	89	100	98	—	78	47	69
Sweetgum	51	28	86	92	58	23	67	69	69
Sycamore	22	12	85	98	96	21	29	79	74
Tanoak	80	39	81	100	100	—	—	—	—
Tupelo, water	55	52	79	62	33	34	46	64	63
Tupelo, black	48	32	75	82	24	21	42	65	63
Walnut, black	62	34	91	100	98	—	78	50	59
Willow	52	5	58	71	24	24	73	89	62
Yellow-poplar	70	13	81	87	63	19	58	77	67

SOURCE: U.S. Forest Products Laboratory, *Wood Handbook.*

5—24 *(near right).* Good grain matching on wide panel.

5—25 *(far right).* Poor grain matching on wide panel.

being prepared. Woods used out of doors had even more stringent requirements. (See "Decay Resistance," p. 128.)

5—26. Continuous door frames and panels.

MATCHING GRAIN

Occasionally a piece of furniture, structurally sound and technically correct, will appear "wrong." It may be right proportionally and yet still look distracting to the eye. Mismatched grain is often the cause of this annoyance. The entire purpose of matching grain is to produce a panel or a series of boards that gives the illusion of being continuous. Correctly matched grain depends on several factors. Experience and a good eye are obviously important. So is the amount of wood available. With several hundred boards to choose from, there is no reason not to obtain the desired number of panels matched for grain pattern and color. If only two boards are available for one panel, the task becomes somewhat more difficult. Yet even with only two boards, sixteen different options are available for gluing them edge to edge! Obviously a board with knots or sapwood on one side limits the choices. As a rule, parallel grain (quartersawn) should not be matched to wide-face grain (plainsawn) or any other grain that runs at an angle to the edge. Figure 5—24 shows a very good match of three parallel-grain to parallel-grain boards; figure 5—25 shows a poor match.

Any extra time spent matching grain and planning the cuttings of adjacent parts is well worth the effort. For instance, cutting a 2-inch (5 cm) face frame for a case out of a 5½-inch (14 cm) board leaves a 3-inch (7.5 cm) strip that can be used as a door stile on that side. If two doors meet in the middle, the two adjacent stiles should be cut from one board. Top rails should be continuous, as should bottom rails. Figure 5—26 shows an excellent example of prior planning to maximize matched grain.

5—27. Five drawers cut from a single board.

The door stiles are continuous, top to bottom on all three doors. Rails are continuous across; in addition, the top rail of one door is cut from the same board as the bottom rail of the door above. Even the three door panels on each side are cut from continuous panels. A well-matched piece is very subtle; a mismatch is painfully obvious at first glance.

Drawers, too, can be matched. Those horizontally adjacent should have their fronts cut from a single piece if possible (figure 5—27). Stacked drawers in bureaus and dressers should have their grain matched as well as possible.

Small slab doors may also have continuous grain, especially if the door is located in a wide board. Figure 5—28 shows an example of a slab door in a tall clock. At first glance it appears extremely difficult to cut a door out of the middle of a wide board, sand all edges, and end up with such a small gap around it. While it can be done with a portable power saw and a handsaw, this is a difficult and time-consuming process that yields only marginally good results. An easier and more precise method is to rip the frame width on either side of the door from the full board on a table saw. This leaves a center section the width of the door. Pass sawn edges over the jointer (at a minimum setting). Locate the door and cut it out of the center board. Finally, reassemble and glue the stock, leaving a space the exact size of the door. After sanding, the glue joints will be virtually invisible. The door can then be hung. Only enough of a gap to allow for opening and closing is required. Wood movement need not be taken into account because the material above and below the

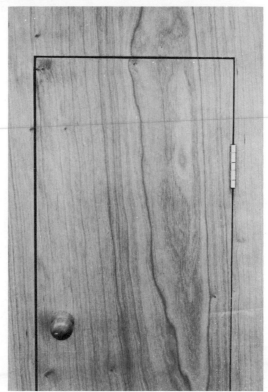

5—28. Slab door cut from a cabinet front.

door shrinks and expands at the same rate as the door itself.

This technique can also be used for matching the grain of drawers set into table skirts. A further refinement is to use a single board for table skirts. This affords continuous grain around the entire table, except for one corner. Even bases under cabinets can be built this way (figure 5—29), as can mirror and picture frames. By carefully mitering (and splining) each corner, a continuous band is produced as

5–29 (near right). Continuous grain around a base.

5–30 (far right). Book-matched doors.

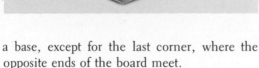

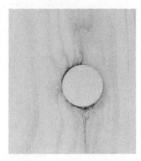

5–31. Wood-filled knot hole.

5–32. Plug-filled knot hole.

5–33. "Grainless" inlay with grain lines drawn in to match.

a base, except for the last corner, where the opposite ends of the board meet.

One of the finest examples of matching grain is book matching. This is most often used on door panels. The panels in figure 5–30 were band sawn from a thick plank and then laid open like the leaves of a book to reveal almost identical grain on both faces. Book matching is especially pleasing on double doors, because of its symmetry.

MINOR IMPERFECTIONS

Large knots, checks, and sapwood (if not desired) should be culled before panels are glued up. Because every single knot and sap pocket cannot be cut out, discretion is required. Small pin knots are often interesting; loose knots, on the other hand, should be filled. There are several methods of filling knots. One requires a small stick of the same wood. Repeated fitting and whittling will make a good "knot," to be glued, pounded into place, and sanded. The finished product looks like a good, tight knot, complete with end grain (figure 5–31). Another method requires a drill and a plug cutter. The knot is drilled out and replaced with a plug, either end grain to accentuate the knot or face grain to try to hide it. If face grain is used, as in figure 5–32, color matching is essential. When a knot that needs to be filled is present in a panel, waste wood from the panel should be saved, since it exactly matches the color.

Sap or bark pockets in woods such as cherry need a different treatment. A commercial wood filler can be used, but it seldom matches the color. A concoction of sanding dust from the board to be repaired, white glue, and a few drops of water can be mixed in a nonmetallic container and applied with a wooden spatula (metal reacts with glue and turns the mixture black). This mix can match any wood color and can be stored for several months in an airtight container. Stick shellac available in a variety of colors can also be melted into sap pockets or other imperfections.

An almost surefire method of matching grain on an inlay is to use no visible grain at all. Instead, select a perfectly flat sawn board, cut it into a diamond, and inlay it over the defect. Sanding follows. Then, with a light-brown pencil, draw in the grain interrrupted by the inlay to match, prior to finishing (figure 5–33).

Dents and nicks in wood often occur during the building process. If the grain is not torn by a sharp edge, then the dent can usually be raised by applying water and allowing it to soak in. The water is then heated by applying a clothes iron, electric hot knife, or even a putty knife heated with a torch to the dent. The water will turn to steam, causing the wood to expand and the dent to disappear.

PATINA, AGING, AND FINISHING

Wood undergoes color change with age. Patina is a photochemical color reaction resulting mostly from light and age, but also from finish and use. Heavy surface finishes drastically slow this action. Hidden under layers of filler, stain, sealer, distressing, and several coats of polyurethane, the wood never has a chance to develop a patina. Some woods are extremely sensitive to light. Cherry, for example, undergoes a rapid photochemical reaction that occurs in the presence of sunlight. Figure 5–34 shows a freshly surfaced cherry board left in direct sunlight with a scraper blade on it for twelve hours. Very often a panel glued up and left near a window will reveal light lines where the clamps have been. Other woods, too, change color with time (figure 5–35).

Usually, very dark woods become lighter and light woods get darker. This, in addition to years of accumulated dust, oils, and dirt worked into the surface, makes it extremely difficult to identify woods in antique furniture.

Finishes also affect the patina. Figure 5–36 shows a piece of cherry cut in half and given two different finishes. The darker half has three coats of boiled linseed oil, while the lighter half has the same number of coats of tung oil and varnish. The picture was taken after about six months of exposure to light. The tung oil and varnish mix contains sun screens that act to retard the natural coloring process. Many surface finishes inhibit patina development.

Surface finishes such as lacquers, varnishes, and polyurethanes do in fact seal the wood and prevent moisture from entering or leaving the wood, but no finish so far developed protects wood 100 percent. Penetrating finishes such as linseed oil, pure tung oil, and some of the new polymerizing oils also afford a degree of protection. The biggest selling feature of lacquer, varnish, and polyurethane seems to be their appearance during the first few years: a lustrous surface impervious to water, alcohol, or food stains. Within a relatively short period, however, time takes its toll, as an increasing number of nicks, scratches, and dents appear. Surface finishes usually cannot be repaired without being obvious.

Penetrating oils require a bit more care (spills must be wiped up within a short time), but are spot repairable. A wet glass left over-

5–34. A scraper blade was left on this cherry board for twelve hours and exposed to sunlight.

5–35. COLOR CHANGES IN AGED WOOD

Species	Original Color	Aged Color
Ash	Light cream	Yellowish light brown
Beech	Light tan	Pinkish brown
Birch	Light pinkish tan	Brown
Black Cherry	Pinkish tan	Deep reddish brown
Red Oak	Reddish tan	Reddish brown
Rock Maple	Light cream	Honey brown
Walnut	Dark brown to purple	Yellow brown
White Oak	Medium tan	Tobacco brown
White Pine	Light cream tan	Orange brown

5–36. The finish affects patina formation. Left cherry half was finished with tung varnish, right half with linseed oil.

night may leave a ring, but it is easily removed with more oil and some steel wool or a cloth. Minor scratches and even burns can be sanded out at any time and reoiled. This may leave a light patch where the patina was broken through, but it soon darkens again. The entire surface can be refinished at any time without paint scrapers or strippers.

Stains are something the honest woodworker may wish to avoid. They are not a canned "magic formula" to turn lowly pine (there is nothing lowly about any wood) into walnut; pine was never intended to look like walnut. Even the "instant age" stains that are supposed

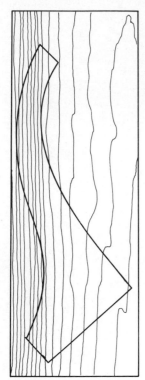

5–37. Curved leg laid out so grain runs between two farthest points.

to make new white pine look like 200-year-old pumpkin pine can be spotted from across the room. These stains have a tendency to highlight every sanding scratch and blemish. Nothing from a can could ever rival the deep, glowing beauty of naturally aged wood.

SHAPING AND FORMING WOOD

Since ancient times forming and bending wood has helped suit the needs of humanity. Wood has been bent for ships, tool handles, agricultural implements, wheels and wagons, barrels, boxes, and baskets. Today wood is still bent for furniture, railings, art work, and even giant trusses for buildings.

Wood is a wonderfully elastic material if chosen and worked correctly. Several methods can bend, shape, and curve wood.

NATURAL FORMS
The easiest way to obtain a curved piece of wood is to saw it out of a larger piece. This is a perfectly acceptable method. When a curved piece is laid out on a straight board with parallel grain, the grain runs out along the edges of the curve. Depending on the severity of the curve and the shortness of the grain running across it, the cutout may have a tendency to break. To minimize the amount of weakness, the grain of the wood should always run between the two most distant points of the curve (figure 5–37).

An even better method is to locate a board with curved grain. In this manner it is possible to match the curved grain to the curved piece to be cut out. Figure 5–38 shows an excellent example of grain matched to the curve of a round-stand leg.

BENDING THEORY
A very thin piece of wood or veneer can be bent to a very tight curve, even back on itself, without breaking. Under ordinary conditions, the thicker the wood being worked, the less it will be able to bend. Figure 5–39 shows a stack of veneer strips bent into a fairly tight circle. The inside piece appears to be longer than the outside piece, but it is not. All are the same length. The inside piece forms a smaller circle with a smaller circumference, while the outside piece forms a larger circle and thus appears shorter. It stands to reason that for any angle, an arc closer to the center will be shorter than one farther away (figure 5–40). One thicker, solid piece of wood will not behave like several thin strips, however, since one side cannot become longer. So if the thicker wood is bent, its length cannot change, as the veneer strips appeared to be doing. Consequently, the grain along the inside curve of the piece is under *compression*, trying to conform to the smaller arc of the inside circle. The grain on the outside of that stick is under *tension*, trying to stretch to the longer arc of the outside circle.

HEAT BENDING
Luthiers often use a process known as heat or dry bending to form wood into shape for guitars, dulcimers, violins, violas, cellos, and lutes. This method works only with relatively thin wood, up to ¼ inch (6 mm) thick. The process involves passing the wood over a hot stovepipe as in figure 5–41. Caution should be used, since the stovepipe, if too hot, can char or burn the wood. An electrically controlled heating iron can be bought for the same purpose.

The side of the wood in contact with the searing heat dries out immediately. As the wood

5–38 *(near right).* Grain matches curve of leg.

5–39 *(far right).* Strips of equal length bent into a circle.

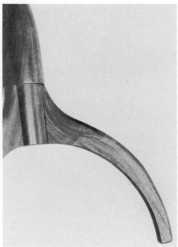

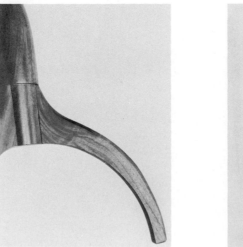

is forced (by hand) into position, the combination of heat and bending causes severe compression in the wood cells. Once cooled, the wood retains its new shape.

STEAMING

Steaming involves the use of heat and steam to plasticize (soften, make flexible and moldable) the wood. Wood cannot be stretched, and it will break under tension. Therefore, the process of steaming is aimed at plasticizing the wood sufficiently so it will compress without failure along the inner radius. Steaming allows compression of 25 to 30 percent beyond normal limits.

Several factors influence the ability of wood to bend: species, moisture content, grain, and defects. Some species of wood lend themselves better to steaming than others. Generally, hardwoods bend much better than softwoods. The hardwoods with the best bending qualities (lowest failure rate or tightest bends) are hackberry, white oak, red oak, elm, hickory, ash, beech, birch, maple, walnut, and sweetgum. Of the softwoods, yellow pine, Douglas fir, redwood, and cedar are most often used, but only for gentle curves.

Moisture content also affects bending. Green wood can be bent well enough but produces problems in seasoning and drying. It is likely to take extremely long to dry and set. Checking, splitting, and shrinkage are also encountered. Very dry wood is not suitable since it must be steamed excessively in order to absorb enough moisture to become sufficiently plasticized for bending. Therefore, a good compromise is wood with a moisture content of 15% to 20%.

When selecting stock for bending, consider the alignment of the grain, as well as any

defects. The grain should be as straight as possible and run parallel to the edges of the stock. Pieces with a grain run-out (grain running diagonally from one edge to the other) of more than 1 inch in 15 (2.5 cm in 38 cm) should not even be considered. With sawn stock, some run-out is inevitable. Traditionally, wood to be bent was rived, or split from heavy stock, to be sure that the grain ran parallel to the edges. Pieces containing *any* knots, checks, pith, brashness, or decay should be discarded. They are certain to fail.

A steam box is easily made of wood or plywood. Exact dimensions depend on the size of the pieces to be steamed. A hinged door should be built into one end. Inside, a wooden rack or series of dowels can be incorporated so that the stock does not lie on the bottom but receives steam from all sides. Ideally the box should be tilted, with a drain hole for condensed water at the lower end.

Almost any steam source that can be directed into the box is suitable. A hose attached to a wallpaper steamer, tea kettle, pressure cooker, or even a sturdy can with a stopper and nozzle can be used, as long as it has a safety valve. The heat source can be electricity, gas, or even wood.

The amount of time allowed for steaming varies. A good starting point is roughly one hour for each ½ inch (1.25 cm) of thickness. The exact time varies with the species of wood and the moisture content of the stock. Kiln-dried wood may need to be steamed two or three times that long.

Once the wood seems to be supple enough, it should be removed from the box and immediately placed in the jig, since cooling and drying start at once.

The form or jig is the heart of the bending

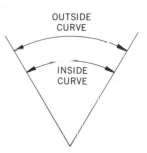

5—40. Relative length of arcs of an angle.

5—41 *(left).* The heat bending of thin wood over a stovepipe.

5—42 *(below).* Steam bending jig with strap and clamps.

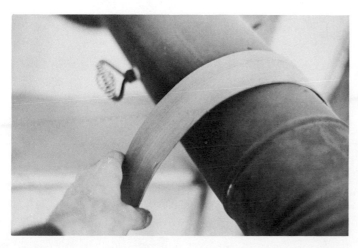

5—43 *(right).* Back and slats of this Shaker rocker were steam bent.

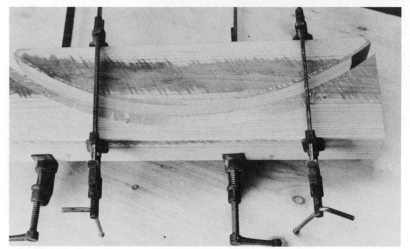

5—44 *(above).* Laminating jig of heavy oak with bar clamps.

tain amount of springback: the wood begins to return to its original shape immediately after being released from the jig. The bending jig must be constructed to compensate for this by overbending. Experiments with several jigs may be necessary to arrive at one that yields the closest desired shape. Figure 5—43 shows a Shaker rocker with steamed posts and back slats.

There are a few other methods of plasticizing wood. Boiling water is sometimes used, most often for small or localized bends, for instance at the end of a very long piece. Steaming is usually preferred, since excessive boiling eventually weakens the wood fibers.

Plasticizing with anhydrous ammonia at $-28°F$ ($-33°C$) seems to hold promise. For the small shop, however, the equipment required is costly, complex, and dangerous.

LAMINATING

Laminating is often easier and certainly more predictable than steaming. Since the individual members are very thin and there is no tension or compression to worry about, very little if any springback occurs. The laminates consist of individual strips or veneers. For small projects the strips can be cut on the saw, using a planer blade to assure a smooth cut. Every effort should be made to reglue the strips in the order they were cut so that the finished product has a more or less continuous grain. For larger projects or small production runs, an entire flitch can be bought from a veneer mill in thicknesses up to 1/10 inch (.25 cm). Since the veneer is cut with a knife and there is no waste between the sheets, laminates glued up carefully make a finished product virtually indistinguishable from a steamed one. All subsequent glue-ups will be identical in shape. Veneer, being as thin as it is, can be bent into extremely small radii of curvature. It is also convenient in testing the bend beforehand.

Jigs for laminating are relatively easy to make. Straps over a frame can be used, but end stops on the straps are not necessary since tension and compression are not encountered. One of the easiest jigs to construct consists of a positive and a negative form cut from a thick block of wood. The two halves are pulled together with bar clamps (figure 5—44). The jig should be coated with wax, silicon, or nonstick tape to prevent excess glue from sticking.

For production runs or more complex bends, a sturdier jig is required. The specific requirements of the bend dictate the exact con-

operation. To a large extent it determines the success or failure of the bend. Since wood does not stretch, a support must be supplied to keep the tension on the outside of the bend under control on severe bends. A steel strap serves the purpose. It should have stops firmly attached at either end to hold the bending stock in place. The strap and wood is then pulled into position around a form that determines the actual shape (figure 5—42).

At least 24 to 48 hours should be allowed for the bend to set. The wood will actually take much longer to really dry but can be placed into a drying jig at that point. A drying jig can be a clamp or a rope to hold the stock in its new shape. It does not have to support it, like a bending jig.

With steam bending, there is always a cer-

struction of the jig. Figure 5—45 shows a steel jig with a nylon strap, used to make the bow of the chair shown in Figure 5—46.

WORKING GREEN WOOD

Most woodworkers have never had a chance to work with green wood. It is an amazing experience, almost like working with an entirely different material. Dry wood is stiff, hard, and unyielding. Green wood is soft and pliable, workable even with the simplest of hand tools.

In the past, most wood was worked green. Only special projects were constructed of dried wood: carvings, furniture to be used indoors, and chair parts. Buildings were constructed of green wood. The heavy posts and beams would have taken years to dry properly. The timbers were simply cut, shaped, and used. In this manner they dried under cover, locked in place by the various joints as well as the building load. The joints stayed tight, when pinned, and movement was allowed for. Green building construction was a matter of necessity.

For other types of wood use, it was a matter of preference. Green wood was pounded into strips for baskets and rived (split) into shingles and slabs. An operation as simple as whittling an ax handle from hickory or ash would have been almost impossible were the wood dry.

Fresh wood also bends with ease. The moisture imparts a flexibility that is lost with drying. Utilizing this property, tool handles, wagon parts, sled runners, and even furniture components were tied into jigs and left for one or two years to season and set in that shape.

One of the more interesting aspects of working green wood involves chair construction. Traditional country chairs of the ladder-

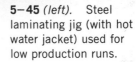

5—45 *(left).* Steel laminating jig (with hot water jacket) used for low production runs.

5—46 *(right).* Chair back made from jig in figure 5—45.

5—47. Chair constructed of green wood.

back or post-and-rung variety were built with a combination of green and dried wood. Using the principles of wood shrinkage, these chairs were made of dried rungs and slats introduced into green posts and legs. The holes around the rungs shrank, leaving a securely locked joint. One of the best books on this method of chair building is John Alexander's *Making a Chair From a Tree: An Introduction to Working Green Wood*. Figure 5–47 shows one of the chairs constructed by this method. The seat is made out of white oak splits, rived and separated while the wood was green.

OUTDOOR WOODWORK

Wooden objects used out-of-doors can last for centuries, or they can crumble in a year's time. The difference lies in knowing which wood to use and how best to use it.

DECAY RESISTANCE
The decay resistance of wood is a direct result of the extractives contained in the heartwood. In nonresistant species the heartwood and sapwood decay at about the same rate. Figure 5–48 groups common native hardwoods into categories of decay resistance.

Only resistant wood, listed in the first column, should be allowed in contact with the ground. Whenever possible, the soil should be well drained. Wooden posts should not be set in concrete, as this forms a water trap and hastens decay.

Moderately resistant woods, from the second column, can be used out-of-doors under ideal conditions, but not in contact with the ground. Good ventilation is necessary.

Least resistant woods from the third column, should not be used out-of-doors at all.

PRESERVATIVES AND WATER REPELLENTS
Builders today rarely build houses with oak, locust, or cypress sills. Instead they use what is available at the lumberyard—pine, fir, or

---

5–48. GROUPING OF SOME DOMESTIC WOODS ACCORDING TO HEARTWOOD DECAY

Resistant or very resistant	Moderately resistant	Slightly or nonresistant
Bald cypress (old growth)[1]	Bald cypress (young growth)[1]	Alder
Catalpa	Douglas fir	Ashes
Cedars	Honeylocust	Aspens
Cherry, black	Larch, western	Basswood
Chestnut	Oak, swamp chestnut	Beech
Cypress, Arizona	Pine, eastern white[1]	Birches
Junipers	Southern pine:	Buckeye
Locust, black[2]	Longleaf[1]	Butternut
Mesquite	Slash[1]	Cottonwood
Mulberry, red[2]	Tamarack	Elms
Oak:		Hackberry
Bur		Hemlocks
Chestnut		Hickories
Gambel		Magnolia
Oregon white		Maples
Post		Oak (red and black species)
White		Pines (other than longleaf, slash, and eastern white)
Osage orange[2]		Poplars
Redwood		Spruces
Sassafras		Sweetgum
Walnut, black		True firs (western and eastern)
Yew, Pacific[2]		Willows
		Yellow-poplar

[1]The southern and eastern pines and bald cypress are now largely second growth with a large proportion of sapwood. Consequently, substantial quantities of heartwood lumber of these species are not available.
[2]These woods have exceptionally high decay resistance.

SOURCE: U.S. Forests Products Laboratory, *Wood Handbook*.

spruce. Under those circumstances a preservative or at least a water repellent is desirable to prevent decay. Preservatives such as creosote and those containing pentachlorophenol are not only expensive but extremely poisonous. Some cannot be used around children, pets, or near water.

The Forest Products Laboratory in Madison, WI, has formulated a simple water repellent for treating wood. It can be mixed at home, is cheaper and not nearly as poisonous as pentachlorophenol, and is just as effective in protecting raw wood from the weather. The treatment: 3 cups (750 ml) exterior varnish; 1 ounce (28.5g) paraffin wax; and enough mineral spirits, turpentine, or paint thinner to make 1 gallon (3.8 l).

AGING AND MOVEMENT OF WOOD

If the correct wood is chosen for outdoor use, it is usually not necessary to treat it. Wood that ages naturally outside turns a silvery gray color. This color results from weathering action, repeated wettings and sun bleachings, and a thin layer of degraded cellulose fibers and microorganisms. Under severely damp conditions, the wood turns greenish black as decay sets in. Ordinarily, wood lasts for decades, losing about 1/4 inch (.6 cm) of exposed surface per century, primarily because of abrasive weathering.

There are a few other points to keep in mind when working wood for outdoor use. Whenever possible, more room should be allowed for shrinkage and expansion, since the moisture range is greater. Quartersawn wood works much better than plainsawn wood because of its reduced shrinkage and expansion and lesser tendency to warp and cup. When board and batten siding is used, the thickness to width ratio of the boards should not exceed 1:8, or excessive cupping is likely to occur. Deck planking should have gaps left to speed drainage and aid drying. Timbers and joists used under decks must be decay resistant and/or treated because of the moisture that collects between these members and the decking.

With sensible practices such as these and access to the right woods, workworkers can expect years of use from their outdoor creations.

BIBLIOGRAPHY

Alexander, John D. *Making a Chair From a Tree: An Introduction to Working Green Wood.* Newtown, CT: Taunton Press, 1978.

Allen, Shirley Walter, and Sharpe, Grant William. *Introduction to American Forestry.* New York: McGraw-Hill Book Company, 1960.

Bois, Paul J. *Constructing and Operating a Small Solar-Heated Lumber Dryer.* Washington, DC: U.S.D.A. Forest Products Laboratory, Tech. Rpt. No. 7, U.S. Government Printing Office, 1977.

Brockman, C. Frank. *Trees of North America.* New York: Golden Press, 1968.

Butler, Robert L. *Wood for Carvers and Craftsmen.* Cranbury, NJ: A.S. Barnes and Company, 1974.

Coleman, Donald G. *Woodworking Fact Book.* New York: Robert Speller and Sons, 1966.

Collingwood, G.H., and Brush, Warren. *Knowing Your Trees.* Revised and edited by Devereux Butcher. Washington, DC: American Forestry Association, 1979.

Constantine, Albert, Jr. *Know Your Woods.* New York: Charles Scribner's Sons, 1959.

Core, Harold A.; Cote, Wilfred A.; and Day, Arnold. *Wood Structure and Identification.* Syracuse, NY: Syracuse University Press, 1976.

Dame, Lorin L., and Brooks, Henry. *The Handbook of Trees of New England.* New York: Dover Publications, Inc., 1972.

Desch, H.E. *Timber: Its Structure and Properties.* New York: St. Martin's Press, 1953.

Edlin, Herbert L. *What Wood Is That: A Manual of Wood Identification.* New York: Viking Press, 1969.

Elias, Thomas S. *The Complete Trees of North America.* New York: Van Nostrand Reinhold Company, Inc., 1980.

Feist, William C. *Protecting Woodwork Without Preservatives.* Washington, DC: U.S.D.A. Forest Products Laboratory, U.S. Government Printing Office, 1980.

Frid, Tage. *Tage Frid Teaches Woodworking, Shaping, Veneering, Finishing.* Newtown, CT: Taunton Press, 1981.

Grim, William Carey. *The Book of Trees.* New York: Hawthorn Books, Inc., 1962.

Henderson, Hiram L. *The Air Seasoning and Kiln Drying of Wood.* Albany, NY: J.B. Lyon Company, 1939.

Hoadley, R. Bruce. *Understanding Wood—A Craftsman's Guide to Wood Technology.* Newtown, CT: Taunton Press, 1980.

James, William L. *Electric Moisture Meters for Wood.* Washington, DC: U.S.D.A. Forest Products Laboratory, Gen. Tech. Rpt. FPL-6, U.S. Government Printing Office, 1975.

Kollman, Franz F.P., and Cote, Wilfred A. *Principles of Wood Science and Technology,* vol. 1, *Solid Wood.* New York: Springer-Verlag, 1968.

McMillen, John M., and Wengert, Eugene M. *Drying Eastern Hardwood Lumber.* Washington, DC: U.S.D.A. Forest Products Laboratory, Agricultural Handbook No. 528, U.S. Government Printing Office, 1978.

Minckler, Leon S. *Woodland Ecology— Environmental Forestry for the Small Owner.* Syracuse, NY: Syracuse University Press, 1975.

Murphey, Wayne K., and Jorgensen, Richard N. *Wood as an Industrial Arts Material.* Elmsford, NY: Pergamon Press, 1974.

Panshin, Alexis J., and deZeeuw, Carl. *Textbook of Wood Technology.* 4th ed. New York: McGraw-Hill Book Company, 1980.

Peck, Edward C. *Bending Solid Wood to Form.* Washington, DC: U.S.D.A. Forest Products Laboratory, Agricultural Handbook No. 125, U.S. Government Printing Office, 1957.

Rasmussen, Edmund F. *Dry Kiln Operator's Manual.* Washington, DC: U.S.D.A Forest Products Laboratory, Agricultural Handbook No. 188, U.S. Government Printing Office, 1961.

Reitz, Raymond C., and Page, Rufus A. *Air Drying of Lumber: A Guide to Industry Practices.* Washington, DC: U.S.D.A. Forest Products Laboratory, Agricultural Handbook No. 402, U.S. Government Printing Office, 1971.

Sargent, Charles Sprague. *Manual of Trees of North America.* 2 vols. New York: Dover Publications, Inc., 1965.

Simmons, Fred C. *Handbook for Eastern Timber Harvest.* Washington, DC: U.S. Department of Agriculture, U.S. Government Printing Office, 1979.

Sloane, Eric. *A Reverence for Wood.* New York: Funk and Wagnalls, 1965.

Stevens, W.C., and Turner, N. *Wood Bending Handbook.* London: Her Brittanic Majesty's Stationary Office, 1970.

Stoddard, Charles H. *Essentials of Forestry Practice.* New York: John Wiley and Sons, 1978.

Symonds, George G.W. *The Tree Identification Book.* New York: William Morrow and Company, 1958.

Tsoumis, George. *Wood as a Raw Material.* Elmsford, NY: Pergamon Press, 1968.

Underhill, Roy. *The Woodwright's Shop.* Chapel Hill, NC: University of North Carolina Press, 1981.

U.S. Forest Products Laboratory. *Wood Handbook: Wood as an Engineering Material.* Washington, DC: U.S.D.A. Agricultural Handbook No. 72, U.S. Government Printing Office, 1974.

U.S. Forest Products Laboratory. *Wood: Colors and Kinds.* Washington, DC: U.S.D.A. Agricultrual Handbook No. 101, U.S. Government Printing Office, 1956.

Wilson, B.F. *The Growing Tree.* Amherst, MA: University of Massachusetts Press, 1970.

INDEX

Boldface indicates pages with complete description and illustration.

Abscission layer, 3
Aerial photos, 76
Agricultural Stabilization and Conservation Service, 96
Alder, 8, 119, 128
Alexander, John, 128
Aliphatic resin glue, 108
American cherry. *See* Black cherry
American chestnut. *See* Chestnut
American elm. *See* Elm
American Forest Institute, 86
American Forestry Association, 86
American holly. *See* Holly
American linden. *See* Basswood
Ammonia, anhydrous, 126
Angiosperm. *See* Hardwood
Apical meristem, 2
Apple (*Malus pumila*), 4, **56–57**, 95
Arborvitae. *See* Northern white cedar
Arizona cypress, 128
Ash. *See* White ash
Aspen, 118, 119, 128
Axes, 81–82

Bald cypress (*Taxodium distichum*), 8, **22–23**, 95, 98, 105, 128
Balsam pine. *See* Eastern white pine
Bark, 3–4, 11
Basswood (*Tilia americana*), 4, 5, 7, 8, **66–67**, 95, 98, 105, 119, 128
Beech (*Fagus grandifolia*), 2, 4, 5, 7, 8, 11, **36–37**, 95, 98, 99, 105, 109, 119, 123, 128
Beetree. *See* Basswood
Belsaw one-man sawmill, 94
Bending, 124–26
Big pine. *See* Sugar pine
Bilstead. *See* Sweet gum
Biltmore ash. *See* White ash
Birch. *See* Yellow birch
Bird's eye, 9–10
Black cherry (*Prunus serotina*), 2, 4, 6, 8, 9, 10, **58–59**, 95, 98, 105, 118, 119, 123
Black locust (*Robinia pseudoacacia*), 2, 4, 5, 6, 8, **60–61**, 105, 128
Black oak. *See* Red oak
Black tupelo, 9, 119
Black walnut (*Juglans nigra*), 2, 4, 5, 7, 8, 10, **28–29**, 95, 98, 105, 119, 123, 128
Blister grain, 9
Bois-d'Arc. *See* Osage orange
Bound water, 95
Bow, 10
Bowwood. *See* Osage orange
Branches, 2
Brashness, 12
Bread-boarded ends, 116–17
Buckeye, 128

Buds, 2
Burls, 12
Bur oak. *See* White oak
Butternut (*Juglans cinerea*), 4, 8, **30–31**, 98, 105, 128
Button wood. *See* Sycamore

Cable logging, 88–89
California redwood. *See* Redwood
Cambium, 3, 11
Cane ash. *See* White ash
Cant hook, 82
Carolina hickory. *See* Shagbark hickory
Carotene, 3
Case construction, 110–14
Case hardening, 10, 95
Catalpa (*Catalpa speciosa*), 2, 4, 6, 7, 8, **74–75**, 128
Catawba tree. *See* Catalpa
Cedar. *See* Eastern red cedar; Northern white cedar
Cellulose, 3
Chain saws, 81, 94
Cherry. *See* Black cherry
Chestnut (*Castanea dentata*), 4, 5, 8, 11, **38–39**, 95, 105, 119
Chestnut oak. *See* White oak
Chinkapin oak. *See* White oak
Chlorophyll, 2–3
Cigar tree. *See* Catalpa
Clear cutting, 87
Cleats, 113–14
Close grain, 5
Coastal redwood. *See* Redwood
Color, 7. *See also* Patina
Competition, 79
Compression, 6–7
Compression wood, 13
Conservation Directory, 87
Contact cement, 108
Cooperative Extension Service, 86
Cottonwood, 119, 128
Crab apple. *See* Apple
Creosote, 128–29
Crook, 10
Crotch grain, 10
Cruiser stick, 82–83
Cup, 10, 113

Date plum. *See* Persimmon
Decay, 11, 128
Density, 8
Dents, 122
Diffuse-porous wood, 5
Disease, 85
Dogwood (*Cornus florida*), 4, 5, 6, 8, **68–69**
Drawers, 114–15
Drying
    air, 98–101
    kiln, 102–3

preparing wood for, 98
purpose of, 95
and warping, 10, 95
Drying sheds, 100

Eastern red cedar (*Juniperus virginiana*), 7, 8, 10, 12, **26–27**, 95, 105, 128
Eastern white pine (*Pinus strobus*), 2, 5, 7, 8, 10, **16–17**, 98, 105, 118, 119, 123, 128
Elm (*Ulmus americana*), 5, 8, 9, **44–45**, 95, 98, 105, 119, 128
End checking, 95
Endothia parasitica, 38
Epoxy, 108
Equilibrium moisture content, 96
Extractives, 3, 7, 10, 105, 128

Feather-leaf tree. *See* Northern white cedar
Fiber saturation point, 95
Fibrous roots, 2
Fiddleback, 9
Figure, 8–10
Finishes, 123
Fir, 2, 5, 7, 128
Firewood, 2, 78, 88, 89
Frame and panel construction, 115–16
Free water, 95

Geotropism, 1
Glues, 107–9
Gluing
    basic technique for, 108–9
    cross-grain, 106–7
    drawers, 114–15
    panels, 109–14
    tables, 116–18
Grades
    hardwood, 92, 93
    softwood, 92–94
Grain, 8–10, 110, 120–22
Green wood, 94–95, 127–28
Growth rings, 3, 4
Gulf cypress. *See* Bald cypress
Gummosis, 12, 122
Gymnosperm. *See* Softwood

Hackberry, 119, 128
Hard maple. *See* Sugar maple
Hardwood, 4, 5
Harvest, 87–89
Heartwood, 4, 7
Hemicellulose, 3
Hemlock, 128
Hickory. *See* Shagbark hickory
Hide glue, 107
Holly (*Ilex opaca*), 5, 8, **62–63**, 105
Hornbeam, 5, 8
Horse logging, 88
Hysteresis, 106

Insects, 85

Jointing, 109
Juniper, 128

Kilns, 102–3
Knots, 2, 91, 122. *See also* Pruning

Lamination, 126
Larch, 5, 128
Leaves, 2–3
Lemon walnut. *See* Butternut
Lignin, 3
Lime. *See* Basswood
Locust. *See* Black locust
Log rule, 82–83
Lopping shears, 82
Luster, 7

Magnolia, 5, 119, 128. *See also* Tulip poplar
Making a Chair from a Tree (Alexander), 128
Maple. *See* Sugar maple
Mesquite, 128
Moisture content, 95–98, 101–2
Moisture meters, 102
Molding, 111
Mulberry, 128

Needles, 2–3, 5
Northern pine. *See* Eastern white pine
Northern red oak. *See* Red oak
Northern white cedar (*Thuja occidentalis*), **24–25**, 105, 128

Oak. *See* Red oak; White oak
Odor, 7
Oilnut. *See* Butternut
Oo-soo-ha-ta. *See* Northern white cedar
Open grain, 5
Osage orange (*Maclura pomifera*), 4, 5, 6, 8, **46–47**, 109, 128
Outdoor woodwork, 128–29
Overcup oak. *See* White oak

Parenchyma cells, 4
Patina, 123–24
Peavy, 82
Pecan, 8, 119
Pentachlorophenol, 129
Persimmon (*Diaspyros virginiana*), 4, 6, 8, **70–71**, 105, 109
Phloem, 3. *See also* Bark
Photosynthesis, 1, 2–3
Plainsawn wood, 90–91, 92
Plane tree. *See* Sycamore
Planting bar, 86
Plastic resin glue, 108
Plum, 6
Pigment figure, 10
Pine. *See* Eastern white pine; Sugar pine
Pine-shoot borer, 16–17
Pin oak. *See* Red oak
Pitch, 12
Pith, 4
Plagiotropism, 1
Polyvinyl resin glue, 107–8

Possumwood. *See* Persimmon
Post oak. *See* White oak
Pruners, 82
Pruning, 83–85
Pumpkin pine, 17
Purple cone pine. *See* Sugar pine

Quadractor, 88
Quartersawn wood, 90, 91–92

Radial face, 6
Rays, 4, 5
Reaction wood, 2, 10, 12–13, 118
Red cypress. *See* Bald cypress
Red gum. *See* Sweet gum
Red juniper. *See* Eastern red cedar
Red oak (*Quercus spp.*), 2, 5, 6, 8, 10, 11, **40–41**, 95, 98, 99, 105, 119, 123, 128
Redwood (*Sequoia sempervirens*), 2, 8, 15, **20–21**, 95, 104, 105, 128
Relative humidity, 96–98
Replanting, 85–86
Resin canals, 5, 11–12
Resorcinal formaldehyde, 108
Ribbon grain, 9
Ribs, 114
Rift-sawing, 91
Ring-porous wood, 5
Rings. *See* Growth rings
Rock maple. *See* Sugar maple
Roots, 1–2
Rotholz, 13
Rum cherry. *See* Black cherry

Sapwood, 4, 7
Sassafras (*Sassafras albidum*), 4, 5, 7, 8, **50–51**, 105, 128
Sawing around, 91
Sawmills, 90
    owner-operated, 94
Saws, 82
Saxifrax. *See* Sassafras
Scarlet oak. *See* Red oak
Sealers, 99
Seed tree system (harvesting), 87
Selection method (harvesting), 87
Shagbark hickory (*Carya ovata*), 2, 5, 6, 8, **32–33**, 98, 105, 109, 119, 128
Shellbark hickory. *See* Shagbark hickory
Shelter wood system (harvesting), 87
Shrinkage
    caused by uneven drying, 95
    and extractives, 105
    and gluing, 109–18
    from green to oven-dry, 104, 105
    outdoors, 129
    predicting, 105–6
    radial, 6–7, 104, 105
    and specific gravity, 105
    tangential, 6–7, 104, 105
    and warps, 10
Shumard oak. *See* Red oak
Skidding, 88
Soft pine. *See* Eastern white pine
Softwood, 4–5
Soil Conservation Service, 86

Sourwood, 6
Southern cypress. *See* Bald cypress
Southern red oak. *See* Red oak
Spalting, 11
Specific gravity, 7–8, 105
Splitting mauls, 82
Spruce, 5, 7, 128
Stabilizers, 114
Stacking, 98, 99–101
Stains, 10–11
Stains (applied), 123–24
Star-leaved gum. *See* Sweet gum
Steaming, 125
Stick shellac, 122
Sugar maple (*Acer saccharum*), 2, 4, 5, 6, 7, 8, 9, 10, 11, **64–65**, 95, 98, 105, 109, 118, 119, 123, 128
Sugar pine (*Pinus lambertiana*), 2, 5, 7, 8, 10, **18–19**, 95, 98, 105, 128
Sugar tree. *See* Sugar maple
Sumac, 4, 15
Surface checking, 95
Swamp birch. *See* Yellow birch
Swamp chestnut oak. *See* White oak
Swamp white oak. *See* White oak
Sweet gum (*Liquidambar styraciflua*), 2, 4, 8, 10, 12, **52–53**, 95, 98, 105, 119, 128
Swelling, 106
Sycamore (*Platanus occidentalus*), 5, 8, 9, **54–55**, 95, 98, 105, 119

Tables, 116–18
Tamarack, 128
Tangential face, 6
Tap roots, 2
Taste, 7
Tension wood, 13
Thinning, 79–81
Tiger stripe, 9
Tongs, 87–88
Transverse face, 6
Trees. *See* Wood and trees
Tulip poplar (*Liriodendron tulipifera*), 5, 7, 8, **48–49**, 95, 98, 105, 119, 128
Tuliptree. *See* Tulip poplar
Twigs, 2
Twist, 10
Tyloses, 6

U.S. Government Printing Office, 86
Upland hickory. *See* Shagbark hickory
Ureaformaldehyde, 108

Vessels, 5

Walnut. *See* Black walnut; Butternut; Shagbark hickory
Warps, 10, 95
Water beech. *See* Sycamore
Water repellent, 128–29
Wedges, 82
Weymouth pine. *See* Eastern white pine
White ash (*Fraxinus americana*), 2, 5, 7, 8, 9, 10, **72–73**, 95, 98, 105, 119, 123, 128
White cypress, *See* Bald cypress
White elm. *See* Elm

White holly. *See* Holly
White oak (*Quercus spp.*), 2, 5, 6, 8, 10, 11,
    40–41, 95, 98, 99, 105, 119, 123, 128
White walnut. *See* Butternut
Whitewood. *See* Basswood
White wood. *See* Tulip poplar
Wild cherry. *See* Black cherry
Willow, 5, 6, 118, 128
Willow oak. *See* Red oak
Winch, 88
Wood and trees
    anatomy of, 1–3
    classification of, 4–6
    defects and abnormalities in, 10–13
    properties of, 6–10
    sources of, 89
    structure of, 3–4, 5
    working qualities of, 118–20
Wood filler, 122
Woodlots
    carrying capacity of, 79
    competition in, 79

    diseases in, 85
    harvesting, 87–89
    insect damage to, 85
    inventorying, 76–77
    multiple-use, 78
    planning objectives for, 77–78
    pruning, 83–85
    replanting, 85–86
    thinning, 79–81

Xanthophyll, 3
Xylem, 3

Yellow birch (*Betula allegheniensis*), 4, 5, 8, 9,
    10, 11, **34–35**, 95, 98, 105, 109, 119, 123
Yellow cypress. *See* Bald cypress
Yellow locust. *See* Black locust
Yellow poplar. *See* Tulip poplar
Yew, 128